CHILDCRAFT
THE HOW AND
WHY LIBRARY

ONCE UPON
A TIME

World Book, Inc.
a Scott Fetzer company
Chicago

Childcraft—The How and Why Library
(Reg. U.S. Pat. and T.M. Off.—Marca Registrada)
© 2000 World Book, Inc. All rights reserved. This
volume may not be reproduced in whole or in part
in any form without prior written permission from
the publisher.

World Book, Inc.
233 N. Michigan Avenue
Chicago, IL 60601

© 1996, 1995, 1994, 1993, 1991, 1990, 1989, 1987,
1986, 1985 World Book, Inc. © 1982, 1981, 1980,
1979, World Book-Childcraft International, Inc. ©
1976, 1974, 1973, 1971, 1970, 1969, 1968, 1965,
1964 Field Enterprises Educational Corporation.

International Copyright © 1996, 1995, 1994, 1993,
1991, 1990, 1989, 1987, 1986, 1985 World Book,
Inc. International Copyright © 1982, 1981, 1980,
1979 World Book-Childcraft International, Inc.
International Copyright © 1976, 1974, 1973, 1971,
1970, 1969, 1968, 1965, 1964 Field Enterprises
Educational Corporation.

Childcraft set ISBN 0-7166-0197-4
Once Upon A Time ISBN 0-7166-0151-6
Library of Congress Catalog Card
Number 98-75114
Printed in the United States of America
1 2 3 4 5 6 7 8 9 06 05 04 03 02 01 00

**For information on other World Book
products, visit our Web site at
www.worldbook.com
For information on sales to schools
and libraries in the United States, call
1-800-975-3250.
For information on sales to schools and
libraries in Canada, call 1-800-837-5365.**

Acknowledgments

Aardema, Verna: *Why Mosquitoes Buzz in People's
Ears* by Verna Aardema. Copyright © 1975 by
Verna Aardema. Used by permission of Dial
Books for Young Readers, a division of Penguin
Putnam Inc. and Curtis Brown Ltd.

Arellano, Rafael Ramirez: "Compae Rabbit's Ride"
edited by Rafael Ramirez Arellano from *Folklore
Portorriqueno*, 1926 by permission of Consejo
Superior de Investigaciones Cientificas, Madrid.

Cameron, Ann: "The Pudding Like a Night on the
Sea" from *The Stories Julian Tells* by Ann Cameron.
Text copyright © 1981 by Ann Cameron.
Reprinted by permission of Pantheon Books, a
division of Random House, Inc.

Hearn, Lafcadio: "The Old Woman and Her
Dumpling" from *Japanese Fairy Tales* by Lafcadio
Hearn. By permission of Peter Pauper Press, Inc.

Hill, Kay: "Glooscap and His People" from *Glooscap
And His Magic Legends of the Wabanaki Indians* by
Kay Hill. Originally published by Dodd, Mead &
Co., Inc. By permission of the author.

Mama, Raouf: "The Prince and the Orphan" from
Why Goats Smell Bad and Other Stories from Benin
© 1998 by Raouf Mama. Reprinted by
permission of Linnet Books/The Shoe String
Press, Inc., North Haven, CT.

Oxenbury, Helen: *It's My Birthday* © 1993 Helen
Oxenbury. Reproduced by permission of
Candlewick Press Inc., Cambridge, MA.

Polushkin, *Maria: Mother, Mother, I Want, Another*
© 1978 By Maria Polushkin. Illustrations by
Diane Dawson. Reprinted by arrangement with
Crown Publishers, Inc.

Roy, Ronald: *A Thousand Pails of Water.* Copyright
© 1978 by Ronald Roy. By permission of The
Doe Coover Agency.

Wagner, Jenny: *The Bunyip of Berkely's Creek* by Jenny
Wagner. Illustrations by Ron Brooks. By
permission of Penguin Australia.

Contents

Fairy tales are filled with fairies, giants, elves, and
many magical events.

These stories have been told over and over
by many people for many years.

Enjoy these stories that come from around the world.

Introduction

Once upon a time…When you hear those words, you expect a story. This book, called *Once Upon a Time,* is filled with fairy tales, folk tales, and other interesting stories.

If you are old enough to understand the difference between real and make-believe, you will enjoy the magic of fairy tales and folk tales. The characters in fairy tales are often royal people, such as kings and queens, princes and princesses, or they may be imaginary people, such as elves, but sometimes they are just regular people. The characters usually have some sort of magical adventure in which they learn something, sometimes

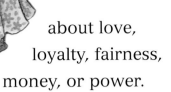

about love,
loyalty, fairness,
money, or power.

Folk tales tell stories about "ordinary folks," or regular people, but sometimes the "folks" are talking animals. Most folk tales are very old. They were told out loud and passed down from parents to children for hundreds of years before anyone wrote them down. In some places, folk tales are still told by storytellers. In folk tales, the endings have a sense of fairness. Kind, hard-working characters are rewarded, and mean, lazy characters are punished.

Other stories may seem more realistic. They have characters who may share your feelings and experiences with growing up.

There are many features in this book to help you find your way through it.

This symbol tells you that a word's meaning is explained.

Each activity has a number. The higher the number, the more adult help you may need.

Growing Food Without Soil

Space stations may grow food in unusual ways. Here's a simple activity you can do on Earth. Sprout your own seeds without soil.

You Will Need:
an empty glass jar
cheesecloth
a rubber band
alfalfa seeds (from a garden store or health food store)
water

What To Do:
1. Sprinkle a single layer of seeds into the bottom of the jar.

A **Try This!** activity has this colorful border.

5

Under some stories, you will see a dictionary symbol: 📖. Following the symbol, you will see how to pronounce a difficult word from the story and what the word means.

This book also has activities that you can do at home. For example, you can make a fairy-tale machine. Look for the words **Try This!** over a colored ball. Review the list of materials needed and read through the instructions before you begin.

Turn to the **Index** to look up page numbers of subjects or stories that interest you.

If you enjoy fairy tales, folk tales, and other stories, look for more in other resources. Here are just a few. Check them out at a bookstore or at the library in your school or town.

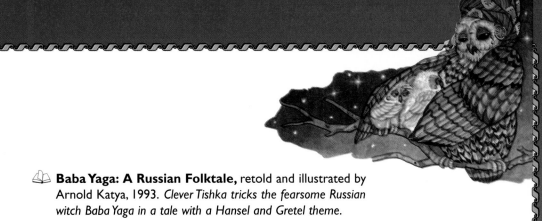

Baba Yaga: A Russian Folktale, retold and illustrated by Arnold Katya, 1993. *Clever Tishka tricks the fearsome Russian witch Baba Yaga in a tale with a Hansel and Gretel theme.*

Children's Bestsellers,
http://www.publishersweekly.com/bsl/currentChildrens.asp
This Web site lets you know what other youngsters are reading today.

Children's Literature Web Guide,
http://www.ucalgary.ca/~dkbrown/
A good place to look for Internet resources related to books, including online stories, information about authors and illustrators, book awards, and lists.

The Great Ball Game, retold by Joseph Bruchac, 1994. *This tale from the Muskogee Indian nation tells how a ball game between the birds and animals settled a dispute.*

The Leopard's Drum, by Jessica Souhami, 1995. *In this Asante tale from West Africa the small tortoise outwits the boastful leopard.*

Lon Po Po: A Red-Riding Hood Story from China, written and illustrated by Ed Young, 1989. *Three brothers mistake the wolf for Po Po, their grandmother.*

The Talking Eggs: A Folktale from the American South, by Robert San Souci, 1982. *A little girl is rewarded for her kindness to an old woman.*

Tales from the Rain Forest: Myths and Legends from the Amazonian Indians of Brazil, retold by Mercedes Dorson and Jeanne Wilmot, 1997. *Myths and legends explore mysteries of life through the eyes of the Amazonian Indians of Brazil.*

Tomie dePaola's Favorite Nursery Tales, written and illustrated by Tomie dePaola, 1986. *Favorite stories for young children.*

It's important to read—alone or with someone else—every day. In case you are wondering where to start, try picking stories about subjects you like, such as animals or imaginary people. The subject index can help you find stories on different subjects. On the next page is a guide to help grown-ups decide what to read with you. It lists all the stories in this book. The groupings show how well readers of different ages may like them or understand them.

Fairy Tales

Everyone loves fairy tales! They tell us about not just fairies, but also elves, trolls, and all kinds of other magical people and events. Some fairy tales teach a lesson. Some have a problem that is solved by magic. And often, there is a bad creature or person to face before the story can end happily.

Jack and the Beanstalk

an English fairy tale

Once upon a time, there was a poor widow who lived with her son Jack and a cow called Milky-White. They sold the cow's milk to pay for their food. Sadly, one morning Milky-White stopped giving milk.

"What shall we do?" cried Jack's worried mother, wringing her hands. "Without the milk we'll have no money, no food!"

"Cheer up, Mother," said Jack. "I'll sell Milky-White, and we'll start a shop with the money."

The next day he rose early and set off, with
Milky-White plodding behind. He hadn't gone
far when he met a funny-looking old man who
said to him, "Good morning, Jack."

"Good morning," replied Jack, wondering
how the man knew his name.

Reaching into his pocket the man pulled out a
handful of brightly colored beans. Holding them
before Jack he said, "As you are so sharp, I
don't mind doing a swap with you—your cow
for these beans."

"Wouldn't you like that!" said Jack.

"Ah!" said the man, "If you plant them
tonight, by morning they will grow right up
to the sky."

Jack thought for a moment. Then he gave the
man Milky-White's lead, pocketed the beans,
and headed home.

 A **swap** (swahp) is a trade or exchange.

"Back already?" said Jack's mother. "How much did you get for Milky-White?" she asked excitedly.

"You'll never guess," said Jack.

On hearing Jack's story, his mother cried, "What! Off to bed with you. There'll be no supper for you. And as for these silly beans, here they go—out the window."

A flickering light awoke Jack early the next morning. His room was being overshadowed by something. He went to the window to investigate. What do you think he saw?

The beans his mother had thrown out the window had grown into a huge, tall, green beanstalk that reached the sky! It disappeared into the clouds.

Edging his way out of the window, Jack grabbed the beanstalk. He climbed higher and higher until he reached the sky. When he got there, he found a long, broad road. He followed it until he came to an enormous house. A big, tall woman stood on the doorstep.

"Good morning, Mum," said Jack,
politely. "Could you be so kind as to give
me some breakfast?"

"It's breakfast you want? It's breakfast you'll
be if you don't move off from here. My man
is an ogre, and there's nothing he likes better
than boys broiled on toast," said the woman.

But she could see that Jack was truly hungry.
Not being as bad as she looked or sounded,
the ogre's wife took Jack in and gave him
bread, cheese, and a jug of milk.

As Jack was finishing his breakfast, there
was a loud **thump! thump! thump!** Quickly,
the woman bundled Jack into the oven to
hide. As she did so, the door swung open
and in strode the giant. He stopped by the
table and sniffed the air.

Fee-fi-fo-fum,
I smell the blood of an Englishman.
Be he alive or be he dead,
I'll grind his bones to have my bread.

"Calm down," said his wife. "You're imagining things. Or perhaps you smell the scraps of that little boy you had for yesterday's dinner. Now sit down and have some breakfast."

Jack sat quietly in the oven, not daring to move for fear of being caught. After breakfast, the giant went over to a large golden chest in the corner and pulled out six bags of gold. As he sat counting, his head began to nod, his eyelids drooped, and at last the sound of snoring shook the house. The giant was asleep.

Seeing his chance to escape, Jack crept out of the oven. Now, being a cheeky fellow, he decided to test his luck. Reaching up, he grabbed a bag of gold from the table, slid down the table leg, and fled as fast as he could from the house to the beanstalk. Then he threw the bag of gold down into his mother's garden and climbed down and down until at last he got home. He showed his mother the gold and said, "Well, Mother, the beans really are magical, you see."

They lived on the gold for some time, but at last it came to an end. So Jack made up his mind to try his luck once more up at the top of the beanstalk.

One fine morning he climbed and climbed until at last he came to the road again and walked up to the enormous house. There, sure enough, was the big, tall woman standing on the doorstep.

"Good morning, Mum," said Jack, as bold as brass. "Could you be so good as to give me something to eat?"

"Go away, my boy," said the big, tall woman, "or else my man will eat you for breakfast. But aren't you the lad who came here once before? Do you know that my man missed one of his bags of gold that very day?"

"That's strange, Mum," said Jack. "I dare say I could tell you something about that, but I'm so hungry I can't speak until I've had something to eat."

Well, the big, tall woman was so curious that she took Jack in and gave him something to eat. But he had scarcely begun munching it—as slowly as he could—when **thump! thump! thump!** they heard the giant's footsteps. "Into the oven with you!" cried the ogre's wife. "You can tell me about the gold when he goes to sleep." In came the ogre, with three great oxen tied to his belt. Throwing them down, he began to sniff the air.

Fee-fi-fo-fum,
I smell the blood of an Englishman,
Be he alive or be he dead,
I'll grind his bones to have my bread.

"Nonsense, dear," said his wife. "It's only the bones of the boy you ate last week. They are still in the garbage."

"Humph! Well, broil these oxen over the fires and I'll have breakfast." After he had eaten, the ogre said, "Wife, bring me the hen that lays the golden eggs." So she brought the hen and the ogre said, "Lay," and it laid an egg made of pure gold.

And then the ogre began to nod his head and snore until the house shook.

Then Jack pushed open the door and crept out of the oven. He caught hold of the golden hen and was off before you could say, "Jack Robinson." But the hen gave a loud cackle, and it woke the ogre up.

Jack ran as fast as he could, and the ogre came rushing after him. The crashing of the ogre's footsteps shook the ground. Jack was quaking with fear as the giant came closer.

Just as the giant was about to grab him, Jack took a flying leap for the beanstalk. Clutching at its leaves, Jack slid down between the branches.

The giant peered down the stalk and decided to follow. The stalk began to tremble with the giant's heavy weight as he made

his way down the stalk. By this time, Jack
had climbed down, and down, and down,
and was nearly at the bottom of the stalk.

Jack called out, "Mother! Mother! Bring
me the ax, bring me the ax!" And his
mother came rushing out with the ax in
her hand.

Jack jumped down to the ground, took
the ax, and started to chop the beanstalk.
The stalk groaned and swayed, and, with a
terrific crash, it fell to the ground, bringing
the ogre with it. That was the end of the
beanstalk—and the ogre.

Jack and his mother sold the golden
eggs that the hen laid. He and his mother
soon became very rich. Jack then married
a beautiful princess, and they all lived
happily ever after.

The Grimm Brothers, Story Collectors

Grimm's fairy tales have been favorites around the world for generations. Jakob and Wilhelm Grimm were brothers. They were born in Hanau, Germany, more than 200 years ago.

The brothers lived and worked together. Jakob studied the history of law and literature of Germany's past. Wilhelm studied stories about heroes and other old texts. Together, they began work on a large dictionary of the German language. The brothers also became interested in folk tales. Many people had heard a few stories, but no one thought the tales were important.

Wilhelm and Jakob collected local tales and legends, especially

Enjoy these tales by the Grimm brothers:

The Bremen Town Musicians
Hansel and Gretel
Rapunzel
Rumpelstiltskin

stories told to children. They also found a peasant woman who knew many more stories and remembered even the smallest details.

Altogether, the two brothers collected 210 stories. They published two volumes, in 1812 and 1815. Scholars paid little attention to the tales, and critics did not think much of them, but other people loved them. The tales were reprinted many times, and within a few years they were translated into 17 languages.

Jakob lived with Wilhelm, his wife Dorthea, and their children, and the two brothers worked together for the rest of their lives. Today, the Grimm brothers are well known as scholars, but they are best known for the tales they collected.

The Shoemaker and the Elves

adapted from a German fairy tale by the Grimm brothers

There was once a shoemaker who worked very hard but was also very poor. At last, all he had was just enough leather to make one pair of shoes. "I hope these turn out well," he said. "If we don't sell

them, we'll have no food for the winter ahead."
He cut out the shoes in the evening so that he
could set to work on them the next morning.
Then he went to bed and, leaving all his cares to
heaven, fell asleep.

In the morning, when he went down to work,
he found the pair of shoes made and finished,
and standing on his table. He was very much
astonished and did not know what to think.

After a moment, the poor man took the shoes
in his hand to look at them more closely. They

were beautifully made. Every stitch was in its right place, just as if they had come from the hand of a master shoemaker.

Soon after, a buyer came in. The beautiful shoes fitted him very well. He gave more than the usual price for them. Now the shoemaker had enough money to buy leather for two pairs of shoes. He cut out the shoes that night, intending to set to work the next morning.

But that was not to be. When he got up in the morning, he found two exquisite pairs of shoes already finished. That day, a customer paid him so much money for the shoes that he was able to buy leather enough for four new pairs.

Early the next morning he found the four pairs finished. And so it continued. Whatever he cut out in the evening was sewn by the morning. He was soon making a good living and was well known for his wonderful shoes.

One night, not long before Christmas, when the shoemaker had finished cutting out shoes, and

before he went to bed, he said to his wife, "How would it be if we were to sit up tonight and see who it is that makes the shoes?"

His wife agreed, and left a light burning. They both hid behind a curtain in a corner of the room and watched to see what would happen.

As soon as it was midnight, two little elves dressed in raggedy old scraps came in and seated themselves at the shoemaker's table. They began to stitch, to pierce, and to hammer so cleverly and quickly with their little fingers that the shoemaker's eyes could scarcely follow them. They did not stop until everything was finished and ready on the table. Then they jumped up and disappeared as quickly as they had come.

The next morning, the shoemaker's wife said to her husband, "Those little elves have helped us so much. We'll never be poor and hungry again. We ought to show our thanks. With all their running about, and having only torn scraps to cover them, they must be very cold. I will make them a dress, a suit, coats and scarves, and some warm socks. And you shall make each of them a tiny pair of gloves and a tiny pair of boots."

The thought pleased the shoemaker very much. So he and his wife set to work. When everything was finished, instead of the cut-out work, they laid the gifts on the table. Then they hid behind the curtain again.

When midnight came, the elves rushed in,
ready to work. But when they found the neat
little garments instead of cut-out leather,
they stood a moment in surprise. Then they
showed the greatest delight. Swiftly, they took

up the clothes and slipped them on, singing, "What spruce and dandy elves are we! No longer cobblers we will be!"

Then they hopped and skipped and leaped over chairs and benches. At last they danced out the door and into the night.

The shoemaker and his wife never saw the elves again. But they always appreciated their help, and from that time, they lived happily ever after.

Hans Christian Andersen, a Storyteller

Hans Christian Andersen died more than a hundred years ago, but his many wonderful stories live on in the hearts of readers. Most are fairy tales he made up, but some are imaginative retellings of folk tales.

Maybe you know his story *The Ugly Duckling*. It tells how a young duckling is unhappy because he doesn't look like his brothers and sisters. They drive him away and he is very lonely. After a long time, the duckling meets some beautiful swans. He wishes he could look like them. Then he sees himself in the water and realizes that he does! He has grown into a fine-looking swan. In fact, he was never a duckling at all.

Andersen's life was much like this story. He was born in 1805 and was the son of a poor shoemaker in Odense, Denmark. He left home at 14 to go to the busy city of Copenhagen, hoping to become an artist. Andersen loved the theater, and he tried hard to find work as a singer, actor, or dancer. But he had a crackly voice and was so tall and awkward that no one would take him seriously.

At last Andersen decided to become a writer instead. He went back to school. He began writing about travel, and his books were popular in Denmark. When his first book of stories was published, he became famous in many other countries too.

Enjoy these tales by Hans Christian Andersen:

The Fir Tree
The Princess and the Pea
The Steadfast Tin Soldier
The Tinder Box
Thumbelina

The Emperor's New Clothes

adapted from a Danish tale by Hans Christian Andersen

Many years ago there was an emperor who was so fond of new clothes that he spent all his money on them. He cared nothing about his soldiers or for the theater, or for driving in the woods, except for the sake of showing off his new clothes. In his palace he

had many rooms full of wardrobes and chests of fine clothes. He liked to admire himself in long mirrors every time he changed. He had a costume for every hour in the day. Instead of saying, as one does about any other king or emperor, "He is in his council chamber," the people here always said, "The emperor is in his dressing room."

Hosts of strangers came to visit the emperor, and among them one day were two swindlers pretending to be weavers. They said they knew how to weave the most beautiful fabrics imaginable. Not only were the colors and patterns unusually fine, but the clothes that were made of their cloth had a magical quality. They were invisible to every person who was not fit for the office he held, or who was a fool.

"Those must be splendid clothes," thought the emperor. "By wearing them I should be able to discover which men in my kingdom are unfit for their posts. I shall be able to tell the wise men from the fools. Yes, I certainly must order some of that cloth to be woven for me."

The emperor paid the two swindlers a lot of money in advance, so that they might begin

📖 A **swindler** (SWIHN dluhr) is a person who cheats other people.

their work at once. The swindlers were given a room in the palace for their work. They put up a loom and pretended to weave, but they had nothing whatever upon their shuttle. They asked for the finest silk and the purest gold thread, all of which they put into their own bags while they pretended to work at the empty loom far into the night.

"I should like to know how those weavers are getting on with their cloth," thought the emperor, but he felt a little queer when he reflected that anyone who was a fool or unfit for his post would not be able to see it. He certainly thought that he need have no fears for himself. Still, he thought he would send somebody else first to see how the work was getting on.

"I will send my faithful minister to the weavers," thought the emperor. "He will be able to see how the cloth looks. He is a clever man, and no one fulfills his duties better than he does!"

So the good minister went to the room where the swindlers sat working at the empty loom.

"Heaven help us," thought the minister, opening his eyes very wide. "Why, I can't see a thing!" But he took care not to say so.

A **shuttle** (SHUHT uhl) is a long wooden or metal container that holds thread for weaving.

Both the swindlers begged him to be good
enough to step a little nearer. They asked if he
did not think it a good pattern and beautiful
coloring, and they pointed to the empty loom.
The poor old minister stared as hard as he
could, but he could not see anything, for of
course there was nothing to see.

"Good heavens!" thought he. "Is it possible that
I am a fool? I have never thought so, and nobody
must know it. Am I not fit for my post? It will
never do to say that I cannot see the cloth."

"Well, sir, you don't say anything about the
cloth," said the one who was pretending to weave.

"Oh, it is beautiful! Quite charming," said the minister, looking through his monocle. "Such a pattern and such colors! I will certainly tell the emperor that the cloth pleases me very much."

"We are delighted to hear you say so," said the swindlers, and then they named all the colors and described the peculiar pattern. The minister paid close attention, so that he could repeat it when he got home to the emperor.

Then the swindlers went on to demand more money, more silk, and more gold, to be able to proceed with the weaving. They put it all into their own pockets. Not a single strand was ever put into the loom. But they went on as before, pretending to weave.

Everybody in the town was now talking about this splendid cloth, and the emperor thought he would like to see it. So, accompanied by a number of selected courtiers, including the faithful official who had already seen the imaginary cloth, he went to

A **monocle** (MAHN uh kuhl) is an eyepiece.
Courtiers (KOHR tee uhrs) are the emperor's attendants.

visit the crafty impostors. They were working as hard as ever at the empty loom.

"It is magnificent!" said the official. "Only see, your majesty, what a design! What colors!" And he pointed to the empty loom, for he thought the others could see the cloth.

"What?" thought the emperor. "I see nothing at all. This is terrible! Am I a fool? Am I not fit to be emperor? Why, nothing worse could happen to me!"

"Oh, it is beautiful," said the emperor. "It has my highest approval." He nodded his satisfaction as he gazed at the empty loom. Nothing would make him say that he could not see anything.

All the emperor's attendants gazed and gazed, but saw nothing more than the others had seen. However, they all exclaimed with His Majesty, "It is very beautiful!" They advised him to wear a suit made of this wonderful cloth for the great procession that was soon to take place.

An **impostor** (ihm PAWS tuhr) is someone who pretends to be something that she or he is not.

"Magnificent! Gorgeous! Excellent!" went from mouth to mouth. The emperor gave each of the weavers a badge of knighthood to be worn in his buttonhole and the title of "Gentleman Weaver."

The swindlers sat up the whole night before the day on which the procession was to take place. They burned sixteen candles,

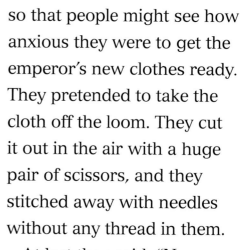

so that people might see how anxious they were to get the emperor's new clothes ready. They pretended to take the cloth off the loom. They cut it out in the air with a huge pair of scissors, and they stitched away with needles without any thread in them.

At last they said, "Now the emperor's new clothes are ready."

The emperor, with his grandest courtiers, went to get them himself. One of the swindlers raised one arm in the air, as if he was holding something. He said, "These are the trousers. This is the coat. Here is the cloak," and so on. "They are as light as a spider's web. One might think one had nothing on, but that is the very beauty of it."

"Yes," said all the courtiers, but they could not see anything, for there was nothing to see!

"Will your imperial majesty be graciously pleased to take off your clothes?" asked the impostors. "Then we may put on the new ones here before the great mirror."

The emperor took off all his clothes, and the impostors pretended to give him one article of clothing after another. They pretended to fasten something around his waist and to tie on something. The emperor turned around and around in front of the mirror.

"How well his majesty looks in his new clothes! How becoming they are!" cried all the courtiers. "What a design, and what colors!"

"Well, I am quite ready," said the emperor. "Don't the clothes fit well?" Then he turned around again in front of the mirror, so that he should seem to be looking at his grand things.

Around the great town, news spread that the emperor would be wearing the finest clothes ever seen in the procession. The crowds gathered to see him. Everyone had also heard that only wise people would see the new clothes, as they would be invisible to fools. Everyone had secretly decided that they would rather pretend to see the clothes than let their friends and neighbors think they were unfit.

As he rode through the streets, the emperor heard the crowds cheering, and thought, "How lucky I am to rule over so many wise people. It seems there are no fools in my country, for everyone can see my new clothes." None of the emperor's clothes had been so successful before.

But there was one small boy who had climbed a tree to get a better view of the emperor. He had not heard that the emperor's new clothes were visible only to wise people, and so had no reason not to tell the truth. The boy shouted out so

everyone would hear, "What has happened to his clothes? The emperor has nothing on at all!"

The people around the boy laughed uneasily at him. Finally, someone else shouted out, "The boy is right! The emperor has got no clothes on!"

Then the whole crowd started laughing, first at the emperor and then at themselves, for they realized they had all been fools to believe the story of the magic clothes.

By this time, the swindlers had left town, taking with them all the money and silk the emperor had given them. And you may be sure they were never seen in that country again.

Then the emperor sent for the little boy in the tree, who had called out. He told the boy he was the only wise person in the whole country, for he was not afraid to speak the truth. The emperor promised the boy that when he grew up, he would be the chief minister.

The Old Woman and Her Dumpling

a Japanese tale by Lafcadio Hearn

Long, long ago there was a funny old woman, who liked to laugh and to make dumplings of rice-flour.

One day while she was preparing some dumplings for dinner, she let one fall, and it rolled into a hole in the earthen floor of her little kitchen and disappeared. The old woman tried to reach it by putting her hand down the hole, and all at once the earth gave way, and the old woman fell in.

She fell quite a distance but was not a bit
hurt. When she got up on her feet again, she
saw that she was standing on a road, just like
the road before her house. It was quite
light down there, and she could see plenty of
rice fields but no one in them. How all this
happened, I cannot tell you. But it seems that
the old woman had fallen into another country.

The road she had fallen upon sloped very
much, so after having looked for her dumpling
in vain, she thought that it must have rolled
farther away down the slope.

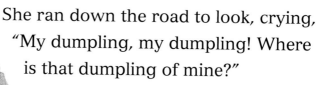

She ran down the road to look, crying, "My dumpling, my dumpling! Where is that dumpling of mine?"

After a little while she saw a stone Fizo standing by the roadside, and she said, "O Lord Fizo, did you see my dumpling?"

Fizo answered, "Yes, I saw your dumpling rolling by me down the road. But you had better not go any farther because there is a wicked Oni living down there, who eats people."

But the old woman only laughed and ran on farther down the road, crying, "My dumpling, my dumpling! Where is that dumpling of mine?" And she came to another statue of Fizo, and asked it, "O kind Lord Fizo, did you see my dumpling?"

Fizo answered, "Yes, I saw your dumpling go by a little while ago. But you must not run any farther because there is a wicked Oni down there, who eats people."

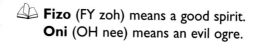 **Fizo** (FY zoh) means a good spirit.
Oni (OH nee) means an evil ogre.

But she only laughed and ran on, still crying out, "My dumpling, my dumpling! Where is that dumpling of mine?" And she came to a third Fizo, and asked it, "O dear Lord Fizo, did you see my dumpling?"

But Fizo said, "Don't talk about your dumpling now. Here is the Oni coming. Squat down here behind my sleeve, and don't make any noise."

Presently the Oni came very close, and stopped and bowed to Fizo, and said, "Good-day, Fizo San!"

Fizo said good-day, too, very politely.

Then the Oni suddenly sniffed the air two or three times in a suspicious way, and cried out, "Fizo San, Fizo San! I smell a smell of mankind somewhere— don't you?"

"Oh!" said Fizo, "perhaps you are mistaken."

"No, no!" said the Oni after sniffing the air again, "I smell a smell of mankind."

Then the old woman could not help laughing—"Te-he-he!"—and the Oni immediately reached down his big hairy hand behind Fizo's sleeve and pulled her out, still laughing, "Te-he-he!"

"Ah-ha!" cried the Oni.

Then Fizo said, "What are you going to do with that good old woman? You must not hurt her."

"I won't," said the Oni. "But I will take her home with me to cook for us."

"Te-he-he!" laughed the old woman.

"Very well," said Fizo, "but you must really be kind to her. If you are not, I shall be very angry."

"I won't hurt her at all," promised the Oni, "and she will only have to do a little work for us every day. Good-bye, Fizo San."

Then the Oni took the old woman far down the road, until they came to a wide, deep river, where there was a boat. He put her into the boat, and took her across the river to his house. It was a very large house. He led her at once into the kitchen, and told her to cook some dinner for himself and the other Oni who lived with him. And he gave her a small wooden rice-paddle, and said, "You must always put only one grain of rice into the pot, and when you stir that one grain of rice in the water with this paddle, the grain will multiply until the pot is full."

So the old woman put just one rice grain into the pot, as the Oni told her, and began to stir it with the paddle. As she stirred, the one grain became two, then four, then eight, then sixteen, thirty-two, sixty-four, and so on. Every time she moved the paddle the rice increased in quantity, and in a few minutes the great pot was full.

   After that, the funny old woman stayed a long
time in the house of the Oni, and every day
cooked food for him and for all his friends. The
Oni never hurt or frightened her, and her work
was made quite easy by the magic paddle—
although she had to cook a very, very great
quantity of rice, because an Oni eats much more
than any human being eats.

But she felt lonely, and always wished very much to go back to her own little house and make her dumplings. And one day, when the Oni were all out somewhere, she thought she would try to run away.

She first took the magic paddle and slipped it under her girdle, and then she went down to the river. No one saw her, and the boat was there. She got into it, and pushed off, and as she could row very well, she was soon far away from the shore.

But the river was very wide, and she had not rowed more than one-fourth of the way across, when the Oni, all of them, came back to the house. They found that their cook was gone, and the magic paddle, too. They ran down to the river at once and saw the old woman rowing away very fast.

Perhaps they could not swim. At all events they had no boat, and they thought the only way they could catch the funny old woman would be to drink up all the water of the river before she got to the other bank. So they knelt down, and began to drink so fast that before

the old woman had got halfway over, the water
had become quite low.

But the old woman kept on rowing until the
water had got so shallow that the Oni stopped
drinking, and began to wade across. Then she
dropped her oar, took the magic paddle from her
girdle, and shook it at the Oni, and made such
funny faces that the Oni all burst out laughing.

But the moment they laughed, they could not
help throwing up all the water they had drunk,
and so the river became full again.

The Oni could not cross, and
the funny old woman
got safely over to the
other side, and ran
away up the road as
fast as she could.

She never stopped
running until she found
herself at home again.

After that she was
very happy, for she
could make dumplings
whenever she pleased.
Besides, she had the magic
paddle to make rice for her.
She sold her dumplings to her
neighbors, and in quite a short
time she became rich.

Make a Fairy-Tale Machine

People have been making up fairy tales for many years. This fairy-tale machine will help you make up tales of your own.

You Will Need:
heavy cardboard, about
   8 inches (20 centimeters) by
   5 inches (13 centimeters)
a file folder
scissors
a pencil or marker

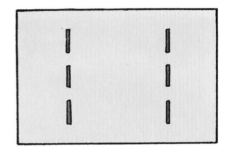

1. Ask an adult to cut six slits in a piece of cardboard, like the one shown above. Each slit should be about 1 1/2 inches (3 centimeters) long.

2. Cut three long strips of cardboard from the file folder. Each strip should be about 1 1/4 inches (2 1/2 centimeters) wide and 14 inches (35 centimeters) long.

3. Thread a strip through each slit on the cardboard. In the window of the first strip, write words for a person, such as *a rich king, a wise frog, a clever girl,* or *a sad magician.* Then slide the strip so that empty paper fills the window, and make up another fun character. Do this until the strip is full of characters.

4. In the window of the second strip, write words that tell what happened, such as *leapt to, lost, forgot,* and *heard.*

5. On the third strip, write words that describe interesting things, such as *a magic key, a pretty queen, golden tennis shoes, a talking cat,* and *three laughing roses.*

6. Use your fairy-tale machine by moving the strips from side to side. Read the words in the windows. They make a sentence that tells what your story will be about. Make up a story. Write it down or tell it to a friend.

For more story fun, take turns with friends. Have one person make a sentence with the fairy-tale machine, and have the next person tell a fairy tale about it!

Cinderella

adapted from a French fairy tale
told by Charles Perrault

Once upon a time, there was a gentleman
who married, for his second wife, the proudest
and most disagreeable woman who was ever
seen. She had two daughters who were exactly
like her in all ways. He himself had a young
daughter, but she was very sweet and good.

No sooner was the wedding over than the
stepmother began to show how mean she really

📖 **Proudest** (PROWD ehst) means most snobbish or stuck-up.

was. She could not bear the good qualities of this pretty girl, who was so unlike her own daughters. So she gave her the hardest and dirtiest work, including washing the dishes and tables, dusting the rooms, and cleaning the fireplace. And the girl had to sleep in a tiny attic room, on a prickly bed of straw.

The poor girl suffered in silence, not daring to tell her father, for he was ruled by his new wife. When she had done her work, she used to go into the chimney corner and sit down among the cinders and ashes. Because of this, her stepsisters gave her the nickname "Cinderella." However, in spite of her shabby clothes, Cinderella was a hundred times more beautiful than her stepsisters, though they always dressed in fine clothes.

It happened that the king's son gave a ball to which all the important people, including the two sisters, were invited. They were delighted, and busied themselves deciding what to wear. This was more work for Cinderella, for it was she who ironed her sisters' clothing and starched their ruffles, while they talked all day long of nothing but their party clothes.

"For my part," said the elder, "I will wear my red velvet suit with trimmings of French lace."

"And I," said the younger, "shall have my usual petticoat. But I will put on my gold-flowered gown and my diamond necklace, which is far finer than anything you have."

Cinderella was often called upon for help, and on the evening of the ball offered to dress them herself and to do their hair. As she was doing this, the elder one said to her, "Cinderella, don't you wish you were going to the ball?"

"Alas," she said, "you are only making fun of me."

"You are right," said the younger one. "It would certainly make people laugh to see a sight as yourself at a palace ball."

After this insult, anyone but Cinderella would have dressed them wrongly, but she was very good and did the job perfectly.

When the stepsisters left for the palace, Cinderella followed the coach with her eyes as long as she could. After it had disappeared, she sat down by the kitchen fire and began to cry.

Instantly, her fairy godmother appeared beside her and asked, "Why all the tears, my child?"

"I wish I could—I wish I could—" Cinderella was not able to speak because of her tears and sobbing.

📖 **Elder** means older person.

"You wish to go to the ball. Is it not so?"

"Yes," cried Cinderella, with a great sigh.

"Well," said her fairy godmother, "be a good girl, and I shall arrange for you to go." Then she said to her, "Run into the garden and bring me a pumpkin."

Cinderella immediately gathered the finest pumpkin and brought it to her fairy godmother. Try as she might, she could not imagine how this pumpkin could get her to the ball. But her fairy godmother took the pumpkin and scooped out all the insides. Then she struck it with her wand, and the pumpkin was instantly turned into a fine coach, covered with gold.

"Now bring me the mousetrap, child."

Cinderella immediately brought the trap, which contained six mice, all alive. The fairy godmother told Cinderella to lift up the little trap door. As each mouse came out, she gave it a little tap with her wand and changed it into a beautiful white horse.

Being at a loss for a coachman, Cinderella said, "I will go and see if there is a rat in the rat trap—we may make a coachman of him."

"You are right," replied her fairy godmother. "Go and look."

Cinderella brought the trap to her, and in it there was a huge rat. The instant the fairy godmother touched him with her wand, he was turned into a big, jolly coachman, who had the finest whiskers imaginable. After that, she said to Cinderella, "Go again into the garden, and you will find six lizards behind the watering pot. Bring them to me."

Cinderella had no sooner done so than her fairy godmother turned them into six footmen. They jumped up behind the coach as if they had done nothing else in their lives. The fairy godmother then said to Cinderella, "Well, you see here everything you need to take you to the ball. Are you not pleased with it?"

"Oh, yes," cried Cinderella, "but must I go in these old rags?"

Her fairy godmother laughed and just touched her with her wand. In that instant, her old rags were turned into cloth of rose and silver, with sparkling golden bows. And on her feet she had a pair of glass slippers, the prettiest in the whole world.

As Cinderella climbed into the coach, her fairy godmother said to her, "Enjoy yourself at the ball, but remember, you must be home by midnight. If you stay one moment longer, the coach will become a pumpkin again. Your horses will be mice, your coachman a rat, your footmen lizards, and your clothes will turn to rags, just as they were before."

Cinderella promised she would leave the ball before midnight. And away she went, hardly able to contain her joy.

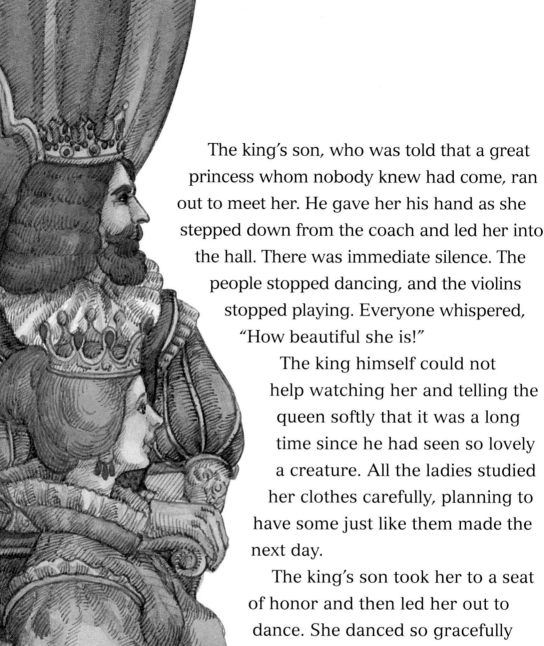

The king's son, who was told that a great princess whom nobody knew had come, ran out to meet her. He gave her his hand as she stepped down from the coach and led her into the hall. There was immediate silence. The people stopped dancing, and the violins stopped playing. Everyone whispered, "How beautiful she is!"

The king himself could not help watching her and telling the queen softly that it was a long time since he had seen so lovely a creature. All the ladies studied her clothes carefully, planning to have some just like them made the next day.

The king's son took her to a seat of honor and then led her out to dance. She danced so gracefully that everyone admired Cinderella more and more. Later, at supper, the young prince ate nothing, he was so busy watching her.

 Admired (ad MYRD) means watched with pleasure and delight.

As for Cinderella, she sat down by her
sisters and showed them every courtesy.
This surprised the stepsisters very much, for they
did not recognize her. Time passed very quickly,
and Cinderella quite forgot what her godmother
had commanded.

A **courtesy** (KUHR tuh see) is a nice, thoughtful deed.

Suddenly Cinderella heard a clock begin to strike, and realized that in a moment it would be midnight. She then rose up and fled, as gracefully as a deer. The prince followed but could not catch her. She left behind one of her glass slippers, which the prince picked up most carefully. Cinderella reached home, quite out of breath and in her old clothes, having nothing left of all her very fancy clothes but one of the little slippers, the mate to the one she had dropped.

The prince asked the guards at the palace gate if they had seen a princess go out. They had seen nobody but a young girl, very poorly dressed.

When the two sisters returned from the ball, they were full of all that had happened. They told of this beautiful girl who had appeared, and who fled as the clock began to strike midnight. And, of course, they spoke of the glass slipper she had dropped in her haste. They said that the prince had picked it up. He had done nothing but look at it the rest of the evening. Most certainly he was in love with the beautiful girl who owned the glass slipper.

What they said was very true. A few days afterward, the king's son announced, with sounds of trumpets, that he would marry the girl whose foot this slipper fit.

The next day, one of the heralds from the court began going from house to house with the glass slipper. One fine woman after another tried it on, but to no avail. It was a fairy slipper and no one could get a foot into it.

Finally, the slipper was brought to the two stepsisters. Each did all she possibly could to get her foot into the slipper. But they could not. Cinderella, who saw all this and knew her own slipper, said to them, laughing, "Let me see if it will fit me."

Her stepsisters burst out laughing. But the herald who brought the slipper said it was only right she should try. He had orders to let everyone try on the slipper.

He asked Cinderella to sit down. Putting the slipper to her foot, he found it went on easily and fitted her as if it had been made of wax.

The two stepsisters were surprised. But they were even more amazed when Cinderella pulled the other slipper out of her pocket and put it on her foot. At that moment, in came her fairy godmother, who touched Cinderella's clothes with her wand and made them richer and more magnificent than any she had worn before.

And now her two stepsisters knew her to be that fine, beautiful lady they had seen at the

A **herald** (HEHR uhld) is a messenger.

ball. They threw themselves at her feet and begged her pardon for all they had said and done to her. Cinderella raised them up and hugged them, saying that she forgave them with all her heart and wished them to love her always.

Cinderella was taken immediately to the young prince. He thought her more charming than ever and, a few days later, married her. Cinderella, who was as good as she was beautiful, gave her two stepsisters a place to live in the palace and before long saw them married to great lords of the court.

The Prince and the Orphan

an African version of Cinderella
translated and retold by Raouf Mama.

My story takes flight over countries and kingdoms of long ago and alights on a prince. He was the king's only son, for all the children before him had died, one after another. Two months before the son was born, the king consulted the oracle according to custom, and this was what the royal diviner said:

"A male child shall be born unto you,

Let his name be a secret to him,

To his mother, and to all your subjects.

Only then shall he dwell

In the world of the living.

When he grows to manhood,

A great many women shall yearn for his love,

But only one has been ordained to claim it.

She shall be his soulmate.

Through their union alone

Can he fulfill his destiny."

Alights (uh LYTS) **on** means comes down and happens upon.
An **oracle** (OHR uh kuhl) or **royal diviner** is a very wise person.
Dwell (DWEHL) means live.
Yearn (YUHRN) **for** means want very much.
Ordained (ohr DAYND) means officially appointed.

When the baby was born, the king held a
secret naming ceremony with only his diviner in
attendance, and the prince was named Denangan,
which means "One of Them Shall Live."

Never was a more handsome prince born to a king, and he grew more handsome still as he drew near adulthood. He was tall and slender with a complexion like the blending of ebony and ivory. His voice was deep, his eyes keen and luminous, and there was a perpetual spring in his step. His smile, which disclosed a shapely row of dazzling white teeth, could touch a heart of stone with joy.

📖 **Keen and luminous** (keen and LOO mih nuhs) means sharp and bright.
A **perpetual** (puhr PEHCH yoo uhl) **spring** means a constant bounce.

What made him the darling of the king's subjects, however, was his kindness and the unusual wisdom that shone through his words and deeds. He was an exceptionally gifted riddle solver. In addition, he was known throughout his father's realm as a champion of the poor and the powerless.

Realm (rehlm) means kingdom.

When the boy grew to be a man and came to desire a wife, the king let it be known that whoever could guess the prince's name would claim him for her husband. The glad tidings of the king's decision spread throughout the kingdom, touching with fire the imaginations of a thousand maidens.

Among these, there was an orphan named Hobami, "Woe Is Me"—the lowliest woman ever to fall in love with a prince. She was a tall, graceful girl with flowing, black hair, and big, brown eyes. Her stepmother, who had three daughters of her own, made Hobami work ceaselessly from the first light of dawn to the hour when witches, draping themselves in the colors of night, filled the air with blood-chilling cries.

Hobami's three stepsisters made no secret of their burning desire to marry the prince and had definite strategies for sweeping him off his feet. Their mother had ordered expensive clothes and jewelry so the sight of them would take the prince's breath away, and she planned to pay a diviner to reveal the prince's secret name.

As the contest drew near and their excitement reached fever-pitch, Hobami's stepsisters grew ever more boastful.

"From the moment the prince sets eyes on me, he will have eyes for no one else," said one.

"My smile will cast such a powerful spell on the prince that he will beg me to marry him on the spot," said another.

"When my turn to say the prince's name comes, my voice will sound so sweet in his ears that he will do anything to keep me by his side all the days of his life," the third sister said.

The voices of Hobami's stepsisters rang in her ears as she set off on one of her interminable errands, and she felt faint. Pressing her palms against her breast, she cried, "I wish I too had a

📖 **Boastful** (BOHST fuhl) means saying too many good things about oneself. **Interminable** (ihn TUHR mihn uh buhl) means endless.

mother who could find me a powerful diviner and dress me up as a princess! Then would my joy know no bounds, for I would not be my stepsisters' laughing stock, but their equal, worthy of the prince's love!" Hobami had no one to give her a helping hand, however, and she had to keep her own counsel.

On the day appointed by the king for the contest, Hobami's stepmother called her three daughters together and handed them the beautiful clothes and the priceless jewels she had bought especially for them. And while the three sisters were jumping up and down and screaming with joy, she called Hobami and gave her a bundle of rags, saying, "The king requires all the young women in the land to take part in the contest this evening. I would like you to dress up like everyone else, but this is all I could afford. You may go as soon as you complete your chores."

And while Hobami was busy drawing water, cleaning dishes, washing clothes, and sweeping the floor, her stepsisters washed themselves, rubbed their bodies with fragrant ointment, and lined their eyelids with antimony. Then, wearing their splendid garments and shimmering jewels, they called Hobami so she could see how beautiful they looked.

📖 **Keep her own counsel** (KOWN suhl) means keep her ideas private.
Antimony (ANT ih moh nee) is a black, silvery powder.

"It's a pity we have
to leave while you are
still doing your chores …
but we will put a palm branch at the
crossroad so you will find your way to the
palace without difficulty," they mocked. Then
they set out for the king's palace and soon came
to the crossroad. They knew that the path to the
right led to the palace, but they put a palm branch
across the path to the left and went on their way.

At the bend in the path, they came upon an old
woman, a spirit in disguise. "My children, give me
something to eat, for I am starving," she pleaded,
holding out her withered hands in supplication.

📖 **Supplication** (suh plih KAY shun) means the act of begging.

"You witch!" one of the sisters snorted. "How dare you call me your daughter!"

"My mother is far younger and much more beautiful than you, old hag!" another sister hissed.

"You get out of our way before I pick you up and throw you into the bush!" the third sister roared. And the three sisters roughly pushed

the old woman aside and moved on, hurling at her any obscenities they could lay tongue to and laughing at their own remarks.

The sun had vanished from the sky and darkness was slowly settling over the village when Hobami completed her final task. Quickly, she washed herself and put on the tattered clothes her stepmother had given her. Then she wrapped a few bean cakes in banana leaves to still her hunger along the way and set out on the long journey to the king's palace.

She soon came to the crossroad her stepsisters had told her about and stood looking now to the left, now to the right, for the palm branch they said they would put across the path leading to the palace. Suddenly a whirlwind arose and enveloped Hobami in an impenetrable cloud of dust. When the dust finally blew away, the palm branch lay across the path to the right. So Hobami turned right and went on her way.

She had hardly gone a few yards when she came upon the same old woman her stepsisters had insulted and ridiculed. The apparition stood across her path, her hands stretched out in

Obscenities (uhb SEHN uh teez) are bad words.
Still (stihl) means to satisfy or hold back.
An **apparition** (AP uh RIHSH uhn) is a spirit or ghost.

supplication. "Give me something to eat, my child, for I am dying of hunger," she implored.

"I do not have much, but the little I have I'll share with you," Hobami replied. So speaking, she unwrapped the bean cakes she had brought with her and gave the old woman an equal share. "Now, if you will excuse me, I must be on my way, for I am late," Hobami said.

"Where are you going so late at night?" the woman asked.

"To the king's palace, to try my luck at guessing the handsome prince's name," Hobami replied.

📖 **Implored** (ihm PLOHRD) means begged.

"But now that I think of it," she went on, "I haven't the foggiest idea what the prince's name is."

"I know the prince's name," the woman said, smiling gently and taking Hobami's hands in her own, "and since you have been so kind to me and given me food, I will tell you. Because all the king's children who were born before him had died in infancy, the king named the prince Denangan, which means 'One of Them Shall Live.'"

Hobami thanked the woman over and over and begged her to say more about the prince, but the woman vanished.

When Hobami reached the royal palace, the last contestant was walking away, her head hanging in shame, to join the sorrowful multitude who had failed the name-guessing test. The sudden appearance of the ragged but comely girl drew sniggers and taunts from all round. Smarting from their own failure and exasperated

📖 **In infancy** (IHN fuhn see) means very young.
Comely (KUHM lee) means pretty.

by Hobami's daring in presuming to succeed where they had failed, the three stepsisters rushed forward and barred her way, their eyes blazing, their hair standing on end.

The king's diviner, who was in charge of the contest, sprang to his feet, ordered the sisters back to their seats, and commanding the crowd to be still, motioned Hobami forward. "Do you know the name of the prince?" he asked her, smiling reassuringly.

"Denangan. That's his name," she stammered, her heart racing out of control. As she fell silent, there broke forth a roll of drums, and a thousand exclamations of wonder and amazement went soaring to the skies. The handsome prince came out from the secret chamber where he had been confined throughout the contest and walked toward Hobami, his arms open wide, his face bathed in a radiant smile.

Ashamed of their lack of kindness and fearful of Hobami's revenge, the three stepsisters and their mother fled from one village to another. But Hobami sought no revenge and left them to their own consciences. The cruelty of Hobami's stepfamily became the subject of numerous songs that followed the fugitives like a curse all the days of their lives. As for Hobami, she and her husband lived a long and happy life and had many children.

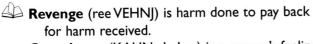

Revenge (ree VEHNJ) is harm done to pay back for harm received.
Conscience (KAHN shuhns) is a person's feelings about what is right and wrong.

Folk Tales and Legends

Some stories are told by so many people for so many years, that they almost seem true! A folk tale is a story told by a group of people. Their children learn it and tell it to their own children. A legend sometimes begins as a story about a real person. But when people tell the story, they make the person especially strong or brave or wise.

The Little Red Hen

an English folk tale

One day Little Red Hen was scratching in the farmyard, when she found a grain of wheat.

"Who will plant the wheat?" said she.

"Not I," said the duck.

"Not I," said the cat.

"Not I," said the dog.

"Very well then," said Little Red Hen, "I will." So she planted the grain of wheat.

After some time, the wheat grew tall and ripe.

📖 **Ripe** (RYP) means ready to harvest.

90

"Who will cut the wheat?" asked Little Red Hen.

"Not I," said the duck.

"Not I," said the cat.

"Not I," said the dog.

"Very well then, I will," said Little Red Hen. So she cut the wheat.

"Now," she said, "who will thresh the wheat?"

"Not I," said the duck.

"Not I," said the cat.

"Not I," said the dog.

"Very well then, I will," said Little Red Hen. So she threshed the wheat.

When the wheat was threshed, she said, "Who will take the wheat to the mill to have it ground into flour?"

"Not I," said the duck.

"Not I," said the cat.

"Not I," said the dog.

"Very well then, I will," said Little Red Hen. So she took the wheat to the mill.

 Thresh (THREHSH) means separate the seeds and grain.

When the wheat was ground into flour, she said, "Who will make this flour into bread?"

"Not I," said the duck.

"Not I," said the cat.

"Not I," said the dog.

"Very well then, I will," said Little Red Hen, and she baked a lovely loaf of bread.

Then she said, "Who will eat the bread?"

"Oh! I will," said the duck.

"Oh! I will," said the cat.

"Oh! I will," said the dog.

"Oh, no you won't!" said Little Red Hen. "I will."

And she called her chicks and shared the bread with them.

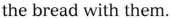

How the Turtle Saved His Own Life

a tale from India
retold by Ellen C. Babbitt

A king once had a lake made in the courtyard for the young princes to play in. They swam about in it and sailed their boats and rafts on it. One day the king told them he had asked his attendants to put some fish in the lake.

Off the boys ran to see the fish. Now, along with the fish, there was a turtle. The boys were delighted with the fish, but they had never seen a turtle, and they were afraid of it, thinking it was a demon. They

📖 A **demon** (DEE muhn) is an evil spirit.

ran back to their father, crying, "There is
a demon on the bank of the lake."

The king ordered his men to catch the demon,
and to bring it to the palace. When the turtle
was brought in, the boys cried and ran away.

The king was very fond of his sons, so he
ordered the men who had brought the turtle
to kill it.

"How shall we kill it?" they asked.

"Pound it to powder," said someone.

"Bake it in hot coals," said another.

So one plan after another was spoken of.
Then an old man who had always been afraid
of the water said, "Throw the thing into the lake
where it flows out over the rocks into the river.
Then it will surely be killed."

When the turtle heard what the old man said,
he thrust out his head and asked, "Friend, what

have I done that you should do such a dreadful
thing as that to me? The other plans were bad
enough, but to throw me into the lake! Don't
speak of such a cruel thing!"

When the king heard what the turtle said, he
told his men to take the turtle at once and throw
it into the lake.

The turtle laughed to himself as he slid away
down the river to his old home. "Good!" he said.
"Those people do not know how safe I am in the
water!"

The Three Billy Goats Gruff

a Norwegian folk tale

Once upon a time there were three Billy Goats Gruff. They lived in a grassy meadow on the banks of a fast-flowing stream. Now there came a time when the grass in their own meadow was almost eaten, and they decided to cross to the other side of the stream where the grass stood tall and thick and juicy.

But first they had to cross the bridge. Under this bridge there lived a great, ugly troll. He had eyes like saucers and a nose as long as a poker.

The first to cross the bridge was the youngest Billy Goat Gruff. *Trip-trap, trip-trap*, he went over the bridge. The troll woke with a snarl when he heard the sound of hoofs.

"Who's that trip-trapping over my bridge?" he roared.

"It's only me, the youngest Billy Goat Gruff," replied the small Billy Goat Gruff in a tiny voice.

📖 A **poker** (POH kuhr) is a metal rod used to stir a fire.

"I'm going over the bridge to eat the long grass in the meadow."

"Well, I'm coming to gobble you up," growled the troll.

"Oh no, please don't eat me," said the youngest Billy Goat Gruff. "I'm so small and skinny. Wait until the second Billy Goat Gruff comes by. He's bigger and fatter!"

"Mmmm," said the greedy troll. "That sounds like a good idea. Over you go then."

A little while later, the second Billy Goat Gruff came across the bridge. *Trip-trap, trip-trap, trip-trap* went his hoofs.

"Who's that trip-trapping over my bridge?" roared the troll.

"It's the second Billy Goat Gruff. I'm going across the bridge to eat the green grass," said the second Billy Goat Gruff in a strong voice.

"Well, I'm coming to gobble you up!" said the troll.

"Oh no, don't eat me. Wait until big Billy Goat Gruff comes by. He's much larger and fatter."

"Oh, all right," said the troll. "If you're sure he'll make a better meal. Over you go!"

Just then, along came the biggest Billy Goat Gruff. *Trip-trap, trip-trap, trip-trap* went his hoofs on the bridge.

"Who's that trip-trapping over my bridge?" roared the troll.

"It is I, the biggest Billy Goat Gruff," said the goat, who also had a very loud voice.

"Well, I'm coming to gobble you up," said the troll, and he leaped up onto the bridge and rolled his greedy eyes in a very frightening way.

But big Billy Goat Gruff lowered his head and rushed at the troll. He butted and poked him with his horns and tossed him off the bridge—*splash!*—into the stream.

And from then on, the three Billy Goats Gruff crossed the bridge every day to feed on the long, green grass on the other side of the stream.

Why the Sun and the Moon Live in the Sky

a folk tale from Africa

Long ago, Sun and Water lived together on Earth. They were great friends. Every day they danced and played together on the beach.

Sun and his wife, Moon, lived together in a warm, cheery house. The house was painted yellow, pink, and gold. Light danced all around it.

Water's house was much larger than Sun's. It was painted blue, green, and violet. A gentle wind blew all around the house, and it was very peaceful.

Sun often went to Water's house, but Water never visited Sun. One day Sun asked Water why he never visited. Water said, "I would like to visit you, but your house is not big enough for me and all my family. If you build a very large new house, my family and I will be happy to visit you."

Sun thought this was a wonderful idea. He and Moon immediately began to build a new house. After a week, the house was finished. It was so big that it stretched as far as the eye could see. The next day, Sun and Moon invited Water to come for a party.

"May I come in?" Water asked when he arrived.

"Of course, dear friend," answered Sun and Moon.

So Water and all the members of his family began to come in the doors. Tiny fish, horseshoe crabs, snails, and huge whales poured into Sun's house.

Soon, Water was knee-deep. "Shall we keep coming in?" Water asked Sun.

"Of course," Sun answered. "The party is just beginning!" So more Water entered the house. Now it poured through the windows as well as the doors.

Soon, Water was high enough to cover a person's head. Again Water asked Sun if he and his family could keep coming in. "Of course!" Sun said again.

Finally, there was so much Water in the house that Sun and Moon had to sit on the roof. "Should we keep coming in?" Water asked.

Sun and Moon were having too much fun to say no. More of Water and more sea creatures poured into the house, until finally it was completely full. Sun and Moon had to go up into the sky, and that is where they have lived ever since.

Why Bear Has a Stumpy Tail

a Norwegian folk tale

One winter day, Mr. Bear met Mr. Fox, who was slinking along with a string of fish he had stolen.

"Hi, stop a minute, Mr. Fox! Where did you get those fish?" demanded Mr. Bear.

Now Fox, as you know, is a sly one indeed. He didn't want Bear to know that he had stolen the fish. So he said, "Oh, my Lord Bruin, we've been out fishing and caught them."

Well, Mr. Bear was hungry and thought he would enjoy some fish. So he asked Mr. Fox to tell him how to go about catching fish.

"Oh, it is quite easy," answered Mr. Fox, "and you'll soon learn. You have only to go down to the river and cut a hole in the ice. Then you put your tail in the hole and keep it there as long as you can.

Don't mind if it hurts a little. That will be the fish biting. The longer you keep your tail in the hole, the more fish you will catch. Then, all at once, pull out your tail. But be sure to give a good hard pull."

Well, Mr. Bear did as Mr. Fox said. Before long, he was very cold and his tail really hurt. But he kept his tail in the hole until he was sure that he must have caught a great many fish.

Then, remembering what Fox had said, he gave a really hard pull. But what he didn't know was that his tail was frozen in the ice. So, when he pulled, his tail snapped off short. And that is why, to this day, Bear has a stumpy tail.

Why Mosquitoes Buzz in People's Ears

a West African folk tale retold by Verna Aardema

One morning a mosquito saw an iguana drinking at a waterhole. The mosquito said, "Iguana, you will never believe what I saw yesterday."

"Try me," said the iguana.

The mosquito said, "I saw a farmer digging yams that were almost as big as I am."

"What's a mosquito compared to a yam?" snapped the iguana grumpily. "I would rather be deaf than listen to such nonsense!" Then he stuck two sticks in his ears and went off, *mek, mek, mek, mek,* through the reeds.

The iguana was still grumbling to himself when he happened to pass by a python.

The big snake raised his head and said, "Good morning, Iguana."

The iguana did not answer but lumbered on, bobbing his head, *badamin, badamin.*

"Now, why won't he speak to me?" said the python to himself.

"Iguana must be angry about something. I'm afraid he is plotting some mischief against me!" He began looking for somewhere to hide. The first likely place he found was a rabbit hole, and in it he went, *wasawusu, wasawusu, wasawusu.*

When the rabbit saw the big snake coming into her burrow, she was terrified. She scurried out through her back way and bounded, *krik, krik, krik,* across a clearing.

📖 **Lumbered** (LUHM burd) means moved slowly and noisily. **Plotting** (PLAH ting) means planning.

A crow saw the rabbit running for her life. He flew into the forest crying *kaa, kaa, kaa!* It was his duty to spread the alarm in case of danger.

A monkey heard the crow. He was sure that some dangerous beast was prowling near. He began screeching and leaping *kili wili* through the trees to help warn the other animals.

As the monkey was crashing through the treetops, he happened to land on a dead limb. It broke and fell on an owl's nest, killing one of the owlets.

Mother Owl was not home. For though she usually hunted only in the night, this morning she was still out searching for one more tidbit to satisfy her hungry babies. When she returned to the nest, she found one of them dead. Her other children told her that the monkey had killed it. All that day and all that night, she sat in her tree—so sad, so sad, so sad!

Now it was Mother Owl who woke the sun each day so that the dawn could come. But this time, when she should have hooted for the sun, she did not do it.

The night grew longer and longer. The animals of the forest

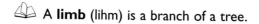

📖 A **limb** (lihm) is a branch of a tree.

knew it was lasting much too long. They feared
that the sun would never come back.

At last King Lion called a meeting of the animals.
They came and sat down, *pem, pem, pem,* around
a council fire. Mother Owl did not come, so the
antelope was sent to fetch her.

When she arrived, King Lion asked,
"Mother Owl, why have you not called
the sun? The night has lasted long,
long, long, and everyone is worried."

Mother Owl said, "Monkey killed
one of my owlets. Because of that,
I cannot bear to wake the sun."

The king said to the gathered
animals:

"Did you hear?

"It was the monkey who killed the owlet—
and now Mother Owl won't wake the sun
so that the day can come."

Then King Lion called the monkey. He came
before the council nervously glancing from
side to side, *rim, rim, rim, rim.*

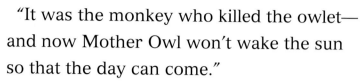

"Monkey," said the king, "why did you
kill one of Mother Owl's babies?"
"Oh, King," said the monkey, "it was the
crow's fault. He was calling and calling to
warn us of danger. And I went leaping
through the trees to help. A limb broke
under me, and it fell *taaa* on the owl's nest."
The king said to the council:
"So, it was the crow
who alarmed the monkey,
who killed the owlet—
and now Mother Owl won't wake the
sun so that the day can come."

Then the king called for the crow.
That big bird came flapping up. He said,
"King Lion, it was the rabbit's fault! I saw
her running for her life in the daytime. Wasn't
that reason enough to spread an alarm?"

The king nodded his head and said to the council:
"So, it was the rabbit
who startled the crow,
who alarmed the monkey,
who killed the owlet—
and now Mother Owl won't wake the sun
so that the day can come."

Then King Lion called the rabbit. The timid little creature stood before him, one trembling paw drawn up uncertainly.

"Rabbit," cried the king, "why did you break a law of nature and go running, running, running, in the daytime?"

"Oh, King," said the rabbit, "it was the python's fault. I was in my house minding my own business when that big snake came in and chased me out."

The king said to the council:
"So, it was the python
who scared the rabbit,
who startled the crow,
who alarmed the monkey,
who killed the owlet—and now
Mother Owl won't wake the sun
so that the day can come."

King Lion called the python, who came slithering, *wasawusu, wasawusu,* past the other animals.

"But, King," he cried, "it was the iguana's fault! He wouldn't speak to me. And I thought he was plotting some mischief against me. When I crawled into the rabbit's hole, I was only trying to hide."

The king said to the council:
"So, it was the iguana

who frightened the python,
who scared the rabbit,
who startled the crow,
who alarmed the monkey,
who killed the owlet—
and now Mother Owl won't wake the
sun so that the day can come."
Now the iguana was not at the meeting
as he had not heard the summons.

The antelope was sent to fetch him.

All the animals laughed when they saw
the iguana coming, *badamin, badamin,*
with the sticks still stuck in his ears!

A **summons** (SUH muhnz) is a formal order or
notice to appear.

King Lion pulled out the sticks, *purup, purup.*
Then he asked, "Iguana, what evil have you
been plotting against the python?"

"None! None at all!" cried the iguana. "Python
is my friend!"

"Then why wouldn't you say good morning to
me?" demanded the snake.

"I didn't hear you, or even see you!" said the
iguana. "Mosquito told me such a big lie, I
couldn't bear to listen to it. So I put sticks in
my ears."

"*Nge, nge, nge,*" laughed the lion. "So that's
why you had sticks in your ears!"

"Yes," said the iguana. "It was the mosquito's
fault."

King Lion said to the council:
"So, it was the mosquito
who annoyed the iguana,
who frightened the python,
who scared the rabbit,
who startled the crow,
who alarmed the monkey,
who killed the owlet—
and now Mother Owl won't wake the sun
so that the day can come."
"Punish the mosquito! Punish the mosquito!"
cried all the animals.

When Mother Owl heard that, she was
satisfied. She turned her head toward the east
and hooted: "Hoo! Hooooo! Hooooooo!"

And the sun came up.

Meanwhile the mosquito had
listened to it all from a nearby
bush. She crept under a curly
leaf, *semm,* and was never found
and brought before the council.

But because of this, the
mosquito has a guilty conscience.
To this day she goes about
whining in people's ears: "*Zeee!* Is
everyone still angry at me?"

When she does that, she gets an
honest answer. KPAO!

Clever Frog

a legend from Brazil

One day, Frog found that he needed a bow. He decided to ask his brother-in-law, Jaguar, to lend him one.

As Frog walked through the village toward Jaguar's house, he met many other villagers. When they saw where he was going, they began to warn him. "If you go into Jaguar's house, he'll eat you," they said.

But Frog went into Jaguar's house anyway. "How are you, brother-in-law?" he called out.

"I'm fine," replied Jaguar, licking his lips hungrily. "Sit down and let's talk."

Frog and Jaguar sat and talked for a long time. The villagers, waiting outside to see what would happen, looked at one another.

"Ah, Frog must want to be eaten," they said. "He's staying in there far too long!"

Jaguar didn't think he could get away with eating Frog with all the villagers watching his house. So he said to Frog, "Brother-in-law, why don't we go down to the river and bathe?"

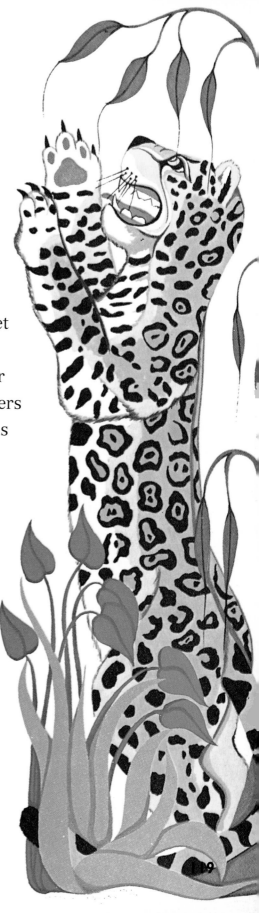

Frog agreed, and they started
out. As they walked, Jaguar kept
trying to get behind Frog so as to
pounce on him. But Frog noticed
this. So he was very careful not to let
his brother-in-law get behind him.

After their bath, Frog and Jaguar
went back to the village. The villagers
were surprised to see that Frog was
still alive.

"Jaguar must be getting soft,"
they whispered to each other.
"He didn't eat Frog while they
were bathing."

It was nearly dark now. Jaguar
turned to Frog and asked,
"Brother-in-law, why don't you
spend the night at my house?"

"Very well," said Frog. But
before settling down for the
night, Frog stepped out of the hut

and caught a firefly. He opened up the firefly and took out the little lantern it carried inside itself. He rubbed the lantern over his eyelids, so that they would shine in the dark when he closed his eyes. Then Frog went back into the house, climbed into a hammock, and went to sleep.

After a while, Jaguar came slinking toward Frog's hammock. Jaguar saw Frog's eyelids shining in the dark. He thought they were Frog's eyes, wide open and looking at him. He quickly turned and crept back to his own hammock.

In the morning, Frog said, "Well, I must be going now, brother-in-law. But before I go, I want to borrow a bow and a flute."

Jaguar gave him the bow and the flute. Frog then walked out into the forest. Jaguar sneaked along after him, keeping out of sight among the trees.

Frog, however, suspected that Jaguar would try to follow him. After a while, Frog came to a tribe of army ants marching across the path. He divided the ants into two groups. He sent each group into the forest, one group on each side of the path.

One group of the army ants soon found Jaguar and began to bite his feet. Jaguar stamped, trying to shake off the ants. From the sound of the stamping, Frog could tell where Jaguar was. He walked into the forest, toward him.

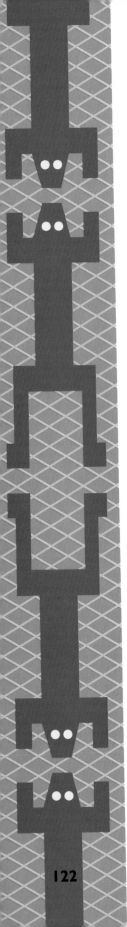

"Hello, brother-in-law," said Frog, softly. "Why are you following me?"

"Why, I was worried about you," Jaguar answered, trying to smile. "I was afraid that some children might harm you."

"It's not the children who want to harm me," said Frog, angrily. "It's you!"

Frog shot an arrow at Jaguar, but he missed. Jaguar dashed away through the trees. He ran through the forest until he reached the village of the snakes.

"Frog is coming this way," he told the snakes. "He's a troublemaker. You ought to kill him!"

The snakes decided to take Jaguar's advice. They hid among the trees beside the path. When Frog appeared, they leaped out. They seized him and took him back to their village.

"Wait a moment," said Frog. "I know you want to kill me. But you'd better not do it here in your village. My blood will flood the place. Kill me on the riverbank, so my blood will go into the water."

So the snakes dragged Frog down to the river. But the instant they let go of him, he dived into the water and vanished. At once, the boa, the anaconda, and all the other snakes jumped in after him. But they couldn't find him.

They couldn't find
Frog because he swam
underwater far up the
river. Then he climbed
out of the river and
climbed up to the
moon. He sat there,
playing the flute he
had borrowed from
his brother-in-law,
Jaguar. When Jaguar
heard Frog playing
the flute, he grew so
angry his eyes flashed.
"Now he's up there
making fun of us!"

And to this day,
Frog is still playing
the flute on the moon.

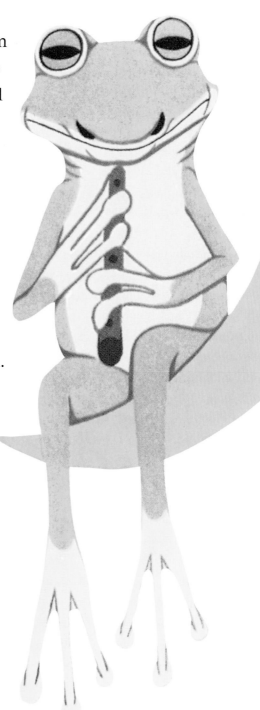

Compae Rabbit's Ride

a Puerto Rican tale by Rafael Ramírez de Arellano

Once Brer Tiger fell in love with Sis Fox, who
didn't so much fall in love with him. Compae
Rabbit learned of it. And he sat himself down and
put his mind to brewing up some devilment—
which wasn't difficult for Rabbit. After a time he
sashayed up to Sis Fox and made a bet with her
that he could ride Tiger horseback past her house.

"Done!" cried Sis Fox, thinking this time Rabbit's
outwagered himself. They shook hands on it.

📖 **Devilment** (DEHV uhl mihnt) means mischief.
Sashayed (sa SHAYD) means moved lightly.
Outwagered himself (owt WAY juhrd hihm SEHLF) means
made a bet that he cannot win.

Well, one day Sis Fox said to Brer Tiger, "Tiger, I feel like dancing. What are you going to do about that?"

"I shall give a dance then, Miss Fox."

"And will you ask Compae Rabbit to play his banjo for us? He is the very best player in the barrio."

"That I will do," said Tiger. And he thought, if Compae comes to play and if during the dance the lights go out and it is pitch dark and if there are scareful noises, then Compae Rabbit just might run down my throat by mistake. Yum!

So Tiger went to see Compae Rabbit about playing his banjo for the dance. And Rabbit said yes, if he were not in pitiful health he would play. Tiger, who had tasty dreams of Rabbit bouncing down his jaws, said, "Then I'll pick you up Saturday."

Come Saturday, Compae Tiger went to find Rabbit. When Rabbit saw Tiger draw near he wrapped up his head with leaves. Around them he wound a big red kerchief till he looked like

📖 **Barrio** (BAHR ee oh) means neighborhood.

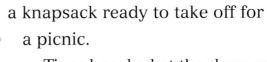

a knapsack ready to take off for a picnic.

Tiger knocked at the door and called, "I've come to get you for the dance, Rabbit."

"Ayyyyyyyyy, Compae Tiger! I am dying and that's a fact. Aches in my tooth. Aches in my head. And besides, a fever is burning me up."

"I will carry you then on my back."

"Very well, Compae Tiger." Rabbit climbed up one side of Tiger and fell off the other. "Ah, Tiger, you see how weak I am? Perhaps if I put on your back an old blanket I have here, I could stay on. What do you think?"

"Place it on."

Rabbit adjusted the blanket, hopped onto it and, pufffff! landed on the ground.

"Ay de mí, it doesn't work at all ..."

"Then, Compae Rabbit, do whatever you have to do in order to hold on."

"Maybe a bridle to hang onto ... and a pair of baskets, one on each side that I will not fall off ..."

📖 **Ay de mí** (ahy duh MEE) is a Spanish saying that means oh my!
A **bridle** (BRY duhl) is a type of harness.

"By all means, lay them on."

So Rabbit harnessed Tiger, setting a bit into his mouth, fastening a rein, and buckling on himself, unseen by Tiger, a fine pair of spurs. Clamping his banjo under his arm, he leaped on Tiger's back. He flicked Tiger with his whip.

"What are you doing, Compae Rabbit?"

"Brushing flies off your neck, Tiger."

Flick, Flick.

"Now what are you doing, Rabbit?"

"Brushing flies off your flank."

Rabbit put the spurs to Tiger.

"What are you doing, Compae Rabbit?"

"I want to go faster. My head
throbs like a bell tolling in a belfry."

Pricking with his spurs and flicking
with his whip, Rabbit had Tiger sprinting
like a racehorse.

They dashed right by Sis Fox's house where
many people stood waiting for the music to
begin. Compae Rabbit saluted Sis Fox with
the whip.

Quickly he hopped off Tiger and tied him to a
fence post like a common horse. Then Rabbit
threw away his sore head and ran inside the house
and commenced plunking the banjo. And everyone
danced—back and forth and round about.

📖 **Tolling in a belfry** (BEHL free) means ringing in a bell tower.

Wolf came by. Poor Tiger said to him, "Compae Wolf, for the sake of heaven will you undo me?"

So Wolf untied Tiger and unsaddled him, and Tiger slunk into the dance. "Compae Rabbit, play us a waltz and play it well," he growled.

"With pleasure, Compae Tiger. But while I play I'm going to sit here by the window where it's breezy and cool."

So Rabbit plunked with all his might while the guests waltzed with all their might. And suddenly the lights went out. And just as suddenly Rabbit went out—the window.

Thus Rabbit won his bet. And Tiger was so humiliated he kept well away from Compae Rabbit and Sis Fox for a long time to come. And that was a blessing for them both.

📖 **Humiliated** (hyoo MIHL ee ay tuhd) means embarrassed.

Glooscap and His People

from Glooscap and His Magic: Legends
of the Wabanaki Indians *by Kay Hill*

In the old time, long before the
white man came, the Indians
believed that every rock and
river, every tree and bird and animal, possessed
a spirit—and some spirits were good and some
were evil. Around these spirits, which they
pictured as giants and wizards and magical
animals, the Indians invented marvelous stories
called *atookwakuns*, or "wonder tales." They tell
these stories to amuse the children, even to this
day, and the stories the children love best are
the stories of Glooscap and his people.

In the beginning, the Indians tell the children,
there was just the forest and the sea—no people
and no animals. Then Glooscap came. Where
this wondrous giant was born and when, they
cannot tell, but he came from somewhere in the
sky with Malsum, his twin brother, to the part
of North America nearest the rising sun. There,
anchoring his canoe, he turned it into a granite

130

island covered with spruce and pine. He called the island Uktamkoo, the land we know today as Newfoundland. This, in the beginning, was Glooscap's lodge.

The Great Chief looked and lived like an ordinary Indian except that he was twice as tall and twice as strong, and possessed great magic. He was never sick, never married, never grew old, and never died. He had a magic belt which gave him great power, and he used this power only for good. Malsum, his brother, also great of stature, had the head of a wolf and the body of an Indian. He knew magic too, but he used his power for evil.

It was the warm time when Glooscap came. As he set about his work, the air was fragrant with balsam and the tang of the sea. First, out of the rock, he made the Little People—the fairies, or Megumooswesoos. These small, hairy creatures dwelt among the rocks and made wonderful music on the flute, such music that all who heard it were bewitched. From amongst them, Glooscap chose a servant, Marten, who was like a younger brother to him.

Fragrant (FRAY gruhnt) means sweet-smelling.
Bewitched (bee WIHCHT) means put under a magic spell.

131

Next Glooscap made men. Taking up his great bow, he shot arrows into the trunks of ash trees. Out of the trees stepped men and women. They were a strong and graceful people with light brown skins and shining black hair, and Glooscap called them the Wabanaki, which means "those who live where the day breaks." In time, the Wabanaki left Uktamkoo and divided into separate tribes and are today a part of the great Algonquin nation—but in the old days only the Micmacs, Malicetes, Penobscots and Passamaquoddies, living in the eastern woodlands of Canada and the United States, were Glooscap's people.

Gazing upon his handiwork, Glooscap was pleased and his shout of triumph made the tall pines bend like grass.

He told the people he was their Great Chief and would rule them with love and justice. He taught them how to build birchbark wigwams and canoes, how to make weirs for catching fish, and how to identify plants useful in medicine. He taught them the names of all the Stars, who were his brothers.

📖 A **weir** (wihr) is a dam across a river.

Then, from among them, he chose an elderly woman whom he called Noogumee, or grandmother, which is a term of respect among Indians for any elderly female. Noogumee was the Great Chief's housekeeper all her days.

Now, finally, out of rocks and clay, Glooscap made the animals—Miko the Squirrel, Team the Moose, Mooin the Bear, and many, many others. Malsum looked on enviously, thinking he too

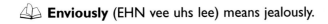 **Enviously** (EHN vee uhs lee) means jealously.

should have had a hand in creation, but he
had not been given that power. However, he
whispered an evil charm, and the remainder
of the clay in Glooscap's hands twisted and fell
to the ground in the form of a strange animal—

not beaver, not badger, not wolverine, but something of all three, and capable of taking any of these forms he chose.

"His name is Lox!" said Malsum triumphantly.

"So be it," said Glooscap. "Let Lox live among us in peace, so long as he remains a friend." Yet he resolved to watch Lox closely, for he could read the heart and knew that Lox had Malsum's evil in him.

Now Glooscap had made the animals all very large, most of them larger and stronger than man. Lox, the troublemaker, at once saw his chance to make mischief.

He went in his wolverine body to Team the Moose and admired his fine antlers, which reached up to the top of the tallest pine tree. "If you should ever meet a man," said Lox, "you could toss him on your horns up to the top of the world."

Now Team, who didn't think things through, went at once to Glooscap and said, "Please, Master, give me a man, so I can toss him on my horns up to the top of the world!"

"I should say not!" cried Glooscap, touching Team with his hand—and the moose was suddenly the size he is today.

Then Lox went in his badger form to the squirrel and said, "With that magnificent tail of yours, Miko, you could smash down every lodge in the village."

"So I could," said Miko proudly, and with his great tail he swept the nearest wigwam right off the ground. But the Great Chief was near. He caught Miko up in his hand and stroked the squirrel's back until he was as small as he is today.

"From now on," said his Master, "you will live in trees and keep your tail where it belongs." And since that time Miko the Squirrel has carried his bushy tail on his back.

Next, the rascally Lox put on his beaver shape and went to Mooin the Bear, who was hardly any bigger than he is today, but had a much larger throat.

"Mooin," said Lox slyly, "supposing you met a man, what would you do to him?" The bear scratched his head thoughtfully. "Eat him," he said at last, with a grin. "Yes, that's what I'd do—I'd swallow him whole!" And having said this, Mooin felt his throat begin to shrink.

"From now on," said Glooscap sternly, "you may swallow only very small creatures." And today the bear, big as he is, eats only small animals, fish, and wild berries.

Now the Great Chief was greatly annoyed at the way his animals were behaving, and wondered if he ought to have made them. He summoned them all and gave them a solemn warning: "I have made you man's equal, but you wish to be his master. Take care—or he may become yours!"

To find out if the animals heeded Glooscap's warning, read the book *Glooscap and His Magic*, by Kay Hill.

138

Stories and Excerpts

We all love to hear a good story. Why? Because stories tell us about life. Sharing stories is a special way in which we can learn about our world.

Mother, Mother, I Want Another

by Maria Polushkin
illustrations by Diane Dawson

It was bedtime in the mouse house.
Mrs. Mouse took baby mouse to his room.

She helped him put on his pajamas and
told him to brush his teeth.

She tucked him into his bed and read
him a bedtime story.

She gave him a bedtime kiss, and then
she said, "Good night."

But as she was leaving,
baby mouse started to cry. "Why
are you crying?" asked Mrs. Mouse.

"I want another, Mother."

"Another mother!" cried Mrs. Mouse. "Where
will I find another mother for my baby?"

Mrs. Mouse ran to get Mrs. Duck. "Please,
Mrs. Duck, come to our house and help put baby
mouse to bed. Tonight he wants another mother."

Mrs. Duck came and sang a song:

Quack, quack, mousie,
Don't you fret.
I'll bring you worms
Both fat and wet.

But baby mouse said, "Mother, Mother, I want another."

Mrs. Duck went to get Mrs. Frog. Mrs. Frog came and sang:

Croak, croak, mousie,
Close your eyes.
I will bring you
Big fat flies.

But baby mouse said, "Mother, Mother, I want another."

Mrs. Frog went to get Mrs. Pig.

Mrs. Pig came and sang a song:

Oink, oink, mousie,

Go to sleep.

I'll bring some carrots

For you to keep.

But baby mouse said,

"Mother, Mother, I want another."

Mrs. Pig went to get Mrs. Donkey.

Mrs. Donkey came and
sang a song:
Hee-haw, mousie,
Hush-a-bye.
I'll sing for you
A lullaby.

But baby mouse had had
enough.
"NO MORE MOTHERS!"
he shouted.

"I want another KISS."

"Really?"

"Well, now!"

"Indeed?"

"I see."

"Oh?"

Mrs. Duck kissed baby mouse.

Mrs. Frog kissed baby mouse.

Mrs. Pig kissed
baby mouse.

And Mrs. Donkey
kissed baby mouse.

Then Mrs. Mouse gave baby mouse a drink of water. She tucked in his blanket. And she gave him a kiss.

Baby mouse smiled. "May I have another, Mother?"

"Of course," said Mrs. Mouse, and she leaned over and gave him another *kiss*.

It's My Birthday

by Helen Oxenbury

"It's my birthday and I'm going to make a cake."

"It's my birthday and
I'm going to make a cake.
I need some eggs."

"I'll get you some eggs,"
said the chicken.

"It's my birthday and
I'm going to make a cake.
I've got the eggs.
But I need some flour."

"I'll get you some flour," said the bear.

"It's my birthday and
I'm going to make a cake.
I've got the eggs and the flour.
But I need some butter and milk."

"I'll get you some butter and milk,"
said the cat.

"It's my birthday and
I'm going to make a cake.
I've got eggs, flour, butter, and milk.
But I need a pinch of salt."

"I'll get you a pinch of salt,"
said the pig.

"It's my birthday and I'm going to make a cake.
I've got eggs, flour, butter, milk,
and a pinch of salt.
But I need some sugar."

"I'll get you some sugar,"
said the dog.

"It's my birthday and I'm going to make a cake. I've got eggs, flour, butter, milk, a pinch of salt, and sugar. But I need some cherries for the top."

"I'll get you some cherries for the top," said the monkey.

"It's my birthday and
I'm going to make a cake.
I've got everything I need."

"We'll all help you make the cake,"
said the chicken, the bear, the cat,
the pig, the dog, and the monkey.

"Thank you, everybody.

Now all of you can...

...help me eat the cake!"

"Happy Birthday!"

The Bunyip of Berkeley's Creek

an Australian story by Jenny Wagner
illustrations by Ron Brooks

Late one night, for no particular reason, something stirred in the black mud at the bottom of Berkeley's Creek.

The fish swam away in fright, and the night birds in the trees hid their heads under their wings. When they looked again, something very large and very muddy was sitting on the bank.

"What am I?" it murmured. "What am I, what am I, what am I?" And the night birds quickly hid their heads under their wings again.

In the morning the thing was still sitting there, scraping the mud off itself to see what was underneath.

"What am I?" it kept saying. "What am I?" But the night birds were all asleep.

A passing platypus solved the problem. "You are a bunyip," he said.

📖 A **bunyip** (BUHN yihp) is a legendary Australian animal.

"Bunyip," murmured the bunyip contentedly.
"Bunyip." Then he sat up straight and called out.
"What do I look like?" But the platypus had
dived into the creek. "Am I handsome?" called
the bunyip. "Am I?" But nobody answered him,
and the bunyip went on sitting there for a long
time, lost in thought.

Presently a wallaby came by to drink at
the creek.

"What do bunyips look like?" asked the bunyip.

"Horrible," said the wallaby. "They have
webbed feet, and feathers."

Contentedly (kuhn TEHNT uhd lee) means happily.
A **wallaby** (WAHL uh bee) is an animal related to
the kangaroo. Some wallabies are 5 feet tall.

"Fine, handsome feathers," said the bunyip hopefully.

"Horrible feathers," said the wallaby firmly, and finished her drink and hopped off.

"Handsome webbed feet?" called the bunyip, but there was no answer. The bunyip sighed and walked off to find someone else.

There was a rustling in the bushes behind him, and suddenly an emu shot past. "Wait!" called the bunyip, running after him. "What do bunyips look like?"

📖 An **emu** (EE myoo) is a large Australian bird that looks like an ostrich. Emus can't fly but they are fast runners.

The emu stopped and considered. "They have fur," he said at last, "and tails."

"How many tails?" asked the bunyip.

"One to each bunyip," replied the emu.

"Fine, handsome tails," said the bunyip.

"Horrible tails," said the emu. "And even more horrible fur." And he settled his feathers and crouched down low, and streaked off into the distance.

The bunyip wandered sadly along the creek. "Will someone tell me what bunyips look like?" he said, to anyone who would listen.

But there was no answer.

Farther along the creek he met a man. The man was busy with a notebook and pencil, and did not look at the bunyip. "Shh," he said, "I'm busy."

The bunyip waited for a long time, and
then he said, very slowly and clearly, "Can
you please tell me what bunyips look like?"

"Yes," said the man, without looking up.
"Bunyips don't look like anything."

"Like nothing?" said the bunyip.

"Like nothing at all," said the man.

"Are you sure?" said the bunyip.

"Quite sure," said the man, and looked right through him. "Bunyips simply don't exist."

The bunyip was shaken. Then he sighed a long, deep sigh. "What a pity," he murmured. "What a pity, what a pity." And he walked

slowly back to his waterhole. Then he fished his belongings out of the water, packed them in his bunyip bag, and walked away. No one saw him go.

The bunyip walked all day, and just as the sun was setting he came to a quiet, still billabong. "This will do," said the bunyip to himself. "No one can see me here. I can be as handsome as I like." And he unpacked his bag, and laid his bunyip comb and mirror out on the sand, and put his billy on to boil. No one saw him and no one spoke to him.

But late that night, for no particular reason, something stirred in the black mud at the bottom of the billabong. The bunyip put his comb down in surprise, and stared. Something very large and very muddy was sitting on the bank.

"What am I?" it murmured. "What am I, what am I?"

The bunyip jumped up in delight. "You are a bunyip!" he shouted.

"Am I? Am I really?" asked the other bunyip; and then, "What do I look like?"

"You look just like me," said the bunyip happily. And he lent her his mirror to prove it.

A **billabong** (BIHL uh bawng) is a pond or small lake.
A **billy** (BIHL ee) is a pot used for cooking over an open fire.

The Pudding Like a Night on the Sea

from The Stories Julian Tells, *by Ann Cameron*

"I'm going to make something special for your mother," my father said.

My mother was out shopping. My father was in the kitchen looking at the pots and the pans and the jars of this and that.

"What are you going to make?" I said.

"A pudding," he said.

My father is a big man with wild black hair. When he laughs, the sun laughs in the windowpanes. When he thinks, you can almost see his thoughts sitting on all the tables and chairs. When he is angry, my little brother Huey and I shiver to the bottom of our shoes.

"What kind of pudding will you make?" Huey said.

"A wonderful pudding," my father said, "It will taste like a whole raft of lemons. It will taste like a night on the sea."

Then he took down a knife and sliced five
lemons in half. He squeezed the first one. Juice
squirted in my eye.

"Stand back!" he said, and squeezed again.
The seeds flew out on the floor. "Pick up those
seeds, Huey!" he said.

Huey took the broom and swept them up.

My father cracked some eggs and put the yolks in a pan and the whites in a bowl. He rolled up his sleeves and pushed back his hair and beat up the yolks. "Sugar, Julian!" he said, and I poured in the sugar.

He went on beating. Then he put in lemon juice and cream and set the pan on the stove. The pudding bubbled and he stirred it fast. Cream splashed on the stove.

"Wipe that up, Huey!" he said.

Huey did.

It was hot by the stove. My father loosened his collar and pushed at his sleeves. The stuff in the pan was getting thicker and thicker. He held the beater up high in the air. "Just right!" he said, and sniffed in the smell of the pudding.

He whipped the egg whites and mixed them into the pudding. The pudding looked softer and lighter than air.

"Done!" he said. He washed all the pots, splashing water on the floor, and wiped the counter so fast that his hair made circles around his head.

"Perfect!" he said. "Now I'm going to take a nap. If something important happens, bother me. If nothing important happens, don't bother me. And—the pudding is for your mother. Leave the pudding alone!"

He went into the living room and was asleep in a minute, sitting straight up in his chair.

Huey and I guarded the pudding.

"Oh, it's a wonderful pudding," Huey said.

"With waves on the top like the ocean," I said.

"I wonder how it tastes," Huey said.

"Leave the pudding alone," I said.

"If I just put my finger in—there—I'll know how it tastes," Huey said.

And he did it.

"You did it!" I said. "How does it taste?"

"It tastes like a whole raft of lemons," he said. "It tastes like a night on the sea."

"You've made a hole in the pudding!" I said. "But since you did it, I'll have a taste." And it tasted like a whole night of lemons. It tasted like floating at sea.

"It's such a big pudding," Huey said. "It can't hurt to have a little more."

"Since you took more, I'll have more," I said.

"That was a bigger lick than I took!" Huey said. "I'm going to have more again."

"Whoops!" I said.

"You put in your whole hand!" Huey said. "Look at the pudding you spilled on the floor!"

"I am going to clean it up," I said. And I took a rag from the sink.

"That's not really clean," Huey said.

"It's the best I can do," I said.

"Look at the pudding!" Huey said.

It looked like craters on the moon. "We have

📖 **Craters** (KRAY tuhrz) are huge holes.

to smooth this over," I said. "So it looks the way it did before! Let's get spoons."

And we evened the top of the pudding with spoons, and while we evened it, we ate some more.

"There isn't much left," I said.

"We were supposed to leave the pudding alone," Huey said.

"We'd better get away from here," I said. We ran into our bedroom and crawled under the bed. After a long time we heard my father's voice.

"Come into the kitchen, dear," he said. "I have something for you."

"Why, what is it?" my mother said, out in the kitchen.

Under the bed, Huey and I pressed ourselves to the wall.

"Look," said my father, out in the kitchen.

"A wonderful pudding."

"Where is the pudding?" my mother said.

"WHERE ARE YOU BOYS?" my father said. His voice went through every crack and corner of the house. We felt like two leaves in a storm.

"WHERE ARE YOU? I SAID!" My father's voice was booming.

Huey whispered to me, "I'm scared."

We heard my father walking slowly through the rooms.

"Huey!" he called. "Julian!"

We could see his feet. He was coming into
our room.

He lifted the bedspread. There was his face,
and his eyes like black lightning. He grabbed
us by the legs and pulled. "STAND UP!" he said.

We stood.

"What do you have to tell me?" he said.

"We went outside," Huey said, "and when we
came back, the pudding was gone!"

"Then why were you hiding under the bed?"
my father said.

We didn't say anything. We looked at the floor.

"I can tell you one thing," he said. "There is
going to be some beating here now! There is
going to be some whipping."

The curtains at the window were shaking.
Huey was holding my hand.

"Go into the kitchen!" my father said. "Right
now!"

We went into the kitchen.

"Come here, Huey!" my father said.

Huey walked toward him, his hands behind his back.

"See these eggs!" my father said. He cracked them and put the yolks in a pan and set the pan on the counter. He stood a chair by the counter. "Stand up here," he said to Huey.

Huey stood on the chair by the counter.

"Now it's time for your beating!" my father said.

Huey started to cry. His tears fell in with the egg yolks.

"Take this!" my father said. My father handed him the eggbeater. "Now beat those eggs," he said. "I want this to be a good beating!"

"Oh!" Huey said. He stopped crying. And he beat the egg yolks.

"Now you, Julian, stand here!" my father said.
I stood on a chair by the table.

"I hope you're ready for your whipping!"

I didn't answer. I was afraid to say yes or no.

"Here!" he said, and he set the egg whites
in front of me. "I want these whipped and
whipped well!"

"Yes, sir!" I said, and started whipping.

My father watched us. My mother came into
the kitchen and watched us.

After a while, Huey said, "This is hard work."

"That's too bad," my father said. "Your beating's
not done!" And he added sugar and cream and
lemon juice to Huey's pan and put the pan on
the stove. And Huey went on beating.

"My arm hurts from whipping," I said.

"That's too bad," my father said. "Your whipping's not done."

So I whipped and whipped, and Huey beat and beat.

"Hold that beater in the air, Huey!" my father said.

Huey held it in the air.

"See!" my father said.

"A good pudding stays on the beater. It's thick
enough now. Your beating's done." Then he
turned to me. "Let's see those egg whites,
Julian!" he said. They were puffed up and fluffy.
"Congratulations, Julian!" he said. "Your
whipping's done."

He mixed the egg whites into the pudding
himself. Then he passed the pudding to my
mother.

"A wonderful pudding," she said. "Would you
like some, boys?"

"No thank you," we said.

She picked up a spoon, "Why, this tastes like
a whole raft of lemons," she said. "This tastes
like a night on the sea."

Be a Storyteller

Have you ever had a wish come true, done something you did not want to do? Have you ever learned to do something really new, or wondered why something is? All these things can give you ideas for stories. Here are some hints that will help you create a story from these ideas.

You Will Need:

paper
pencil
your imagination

What To Do:

1. First, create the beginning of your story. The beginning of a story introduces where or when the story takes place. The beginning also introduces the main character. It tells about something that happens to the character, or a problem the character faces. Make up characters who are like people you know. Have something interesting happen to the main character. It can be something that happened to you or to a friend. Or decide to tell something like why bears have stumpy tails or why worms are slimy.

2. Next, make up the middle of your story. In the middle of a story, the excitement builds up through different events. Readers can't wait to get to the end! Describe the people and places. Try to see them in your mind and write down what you see. Tell what happens as a result of that something interesting.

3. Now, create the ending to your story. The end of the story shows how everything turned out and how the characters felt.

4. Finally, tell your story to yourself. Does it have a good beginning, middle, and end? Interesting stories have all three. Does it describe things? Is it exciting? Make any changes you want, then share your story with a friend. You might even want to draw pictures to go with your story. Enjoy!

A Thousand Pails of Water

A Japanese story by Ronald Roy

Yukio lived in a village where people fished and hunted whales to make their living. Yukio's father was a whale hunter too.

"Why do you kill the whales, Father?" Yukio asked. "Suki's father works in the market and his hands are never red from blood."

"Hunting the whale is all I know," his father answered. But Yukio did not understand.

Yukio went to his grandfather and asked again, "Why does my father kill the whales?"

"Your father does what he must do," his grandfather said. "Let him be, little one, and ask your questions of the sea."

So Yukio went to the sea.

Small creatures scurried from under his feet in the tide pools. Large scavenger birds screamed at him from the sky.

Then Yukio saw a whale that had become lodged between some rocks and was left behind when the tide went out.

The large tail flukes beat the sand helplessly. The eye, as big as Yukio's hand, rolled in fright.

A **scavenger** (SKAV uhn juhr) eats dead or decaying materials.

Flukes (flooks) are the two halves of a whale's tail.

Yukio knew the whale would not live long out of the sea.

"I will help you, sir," he said.

But how? The whale was huge, like a temple.

Yukio raced to the water's edge. Was the tide coming in or going out? In, he decided, by the way the little fingers of foam climbed higher with each new wave.

The sun was hot on Yukio's back as he looked at the whale.

Yukio filled his pail with water and threw it over the great head.

"You are so big and my pail is so small!" he
cried. "But I will throw a thousand pails of water
over you before I stop."

The second pail went on the head as well, and
the third and the fourth. But Yukio knew he
must wet every part of the whale or it would die
in the sun.

Yukio made many trips to the sea for water,
counting as he went. He threw four pails on the
body, and then four on the tail, and then three

on the head. How many had he filled so far? He had lost count. But he knew he must not stop.

There was a little shade on one side of the big gray prisoner. Yukio sat there out of breath, his heart pounding. Then he looked in the whale's eye and remembered his promise.

Yukio filled his pail over and over. His back hurt and his arms—but he threw and threw. He fell down and he did not get up. Yukio felt himself being lifted.

"You have worked hard, little one. Now let us help."

Yukio's grandfather laid him in the shade of one of the rocks. Yukio watched his grandfather throw his first pail of water and go for another.

"Hurry!" Yukio wanted to scream, for his grandfather was old and walked slowly.

Then Yukio heard voices. His father and the village people were running toward the sea. They carried pails and buckets and anything that would hold water.

Some of the villagers removed their jackets and soaked them in the sea. These they placed on the whale's burning skin. Soon the whale was wet all over.

Slowly the sea came closer and closer. At last it covered the huge tail. The village people ran back and forth carrying water, shouting to each other. Yukio knew the whale would be safe.

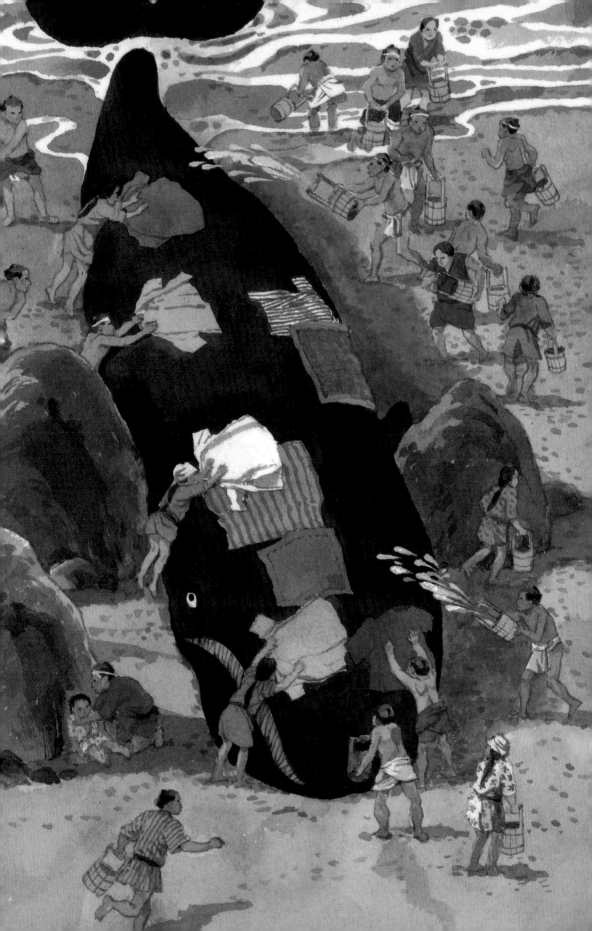

Yukio's father came and stood by him.
"Thank you, Father," Yukio said, "for bringing
the village people to help."
"You are strong and good," his father said.
"But to save a whale, many hands must carry
the water."

Now the whale was moving with each new wave. Suddenly a great one lifted him free of the rocks. He was still for a moment, then, with a flip of his tail, swam out to sea.

The villagers watched silently, as the whale swam farther and farther from their shore. Then they turned and walked toward the village.

Except for Yukio, who was asleep in the arms of his father.

He had carried a thousand pails of water and he was tired.

Index by Author

If you know the name of the author you are looking for, use this index. You can also find a story by using the **Index by Title** on this page or the **Index by Subject** on page 191. For stories in all other volumes, see the entry **stories** in the General Index in Volume 15.

Index by Title

If you know the title of the story you are looking for, use this index. You can also find a story by using the **Index by Author** on this page or the **Index by Subject** on page 191. For stories in all other volumes, see the entry **stories** in the General Index in Volume 15.

Index by Subject

Use this index to find a story about a particular subject. You can also find a story by using the **Index by Author** on page 190 or the **Index by Title** on page 190. For stories in all other volumes, see the entry **stories** in the General Index in Volume 15.

Illustration Acknowledgments

The Publishers of *Childcraft* gratefully acknowledge the courtesy of the following illustrators, photographers, agencies, and organizations for illustrations in this volume. When all the illustrations for a sequence of pages are from a single source, the inclusive page numbers are given. Credits should be read from top to bottom, left to right on their respective pages. All illustrations are the exclusive property of the publishers of *Childcraft* unless names are marked with an asterisk (*).

Cover Princess and frog—© James Balog, Tony Stone Images*; Hen—Robert Byrd; Frog—Dan B. Timmons
Back Cover Dan B. Timmons
1 Robert Byrd; Dan B. Timmons
2-3 Kate Salley Palmer; Lydia Halverson; Jan Brett; Marlene Ekman
4-5 Diane Dawson
6-7 Yoshi Miyake; Janice Skivington; Nan Brooks; Jan Brett; Robert Byrd
10-11 Yoshi Miyake; Jerry Pinkney; Lydia Halverson; Marlene Ekman
12-21 Jerry Pinkney

22-23 Lydia Halverson
24-33 Yoshi Miyake
34-35 Tony Herbert
36-39 Drew-Brook-Cormack Associates
40-41 Lydia Halverson
42-47 Drew-Brook-Cormack Associates
48-57 Marlene Ekman
58-59 Eileen Mueller Neill
60-73 Yoshi Miyake
74-87 Janice Skivington
88-89 Gwen Connelly; Jerry Pinkney; Jan Brett; Robert Byrd
90-91 Robert Byrd
92-93 Robert Byrd; Jerry Pinkney
94-95 Jerry Pinkney
96-99 Kinuko Craft

100-105 Gwen Connelly
106-107 Robert Byrd
108-117 Jan Brett
118-123 Dan B. Timmons
124-129 Richard Laurent
130-137 Bert Dodson; Ben Manchipp
138-139 Mou-sien Tseng; Kate Salley Palmer; Diane Dawson; Nan Brooks
140-147 Diane Dawson
148-157 Nan Brooks
158-165 Ron Brooks*
166-177 Kate Salley Palmer
178-179 Eileen Mueller Neill
180-181 Lydia Halverson
182-189 Mou-sien Tseng